SADLIER

VOCABULARY WORKSHOP®

ACHIEVE

Jerome Shostak

Senior Series Consultant

Vicki A. Jacobs, Ed.D.
Lecturer on Education
Harvard Graduate School of Education
Cambridge, Massachusetts

Series Consultants

Louis P. De Angelo, Ed.D.
Superintendent of Schools
Diocese of Wilmington
Wilmington, Delaware

John Heath, Ph.D.
Professor of Classics
Santa Clara University
Santa Clara, California

Sarah Ressler Wright, M.A. English Ed, NBCT
Head Librarian
Rutherford B. Hayes High School
Delaware, Ohio

Carolyn E. Waters, J.D., Ed.S.
Georgia Dept. of Education (Ret.)
English Language Arts Consultant
Woodstock, Georgia

Reviewers

The publisher wishes to thank for their comments and suggestions the following teachers and administrators, who read portions of the series prior to publication.

Ronald Apperson
Teacher
George Fox Middle School
Pasadena, MD

Rebecca Benjamin
English Teacher
Island Trees Memorial Middle School
Levittown, NY

Heidi Branch
8th Grade English Teacher,
Department Chair
Belmont Ridge Middle School
Leesburg, VA

Lynne W. Jansen
ELA Instructor
Landrum Middle School
Ponte Vedra, FL

Kasandra Washington
School Counselor
Former ELA Instructor
Manor Middle School
Manor, TX

Cover: Concept/Art and Design: MK Advertising, Studio Montage and William H. Sadlier, Inc. Cover pencil: Shutterstock.com/VikaSuh. **Photo Credits**: akg-images: 116. Alamy Stock Photo/imageZebra: 80–81; JLImages: 76; WoodyStock: 44; Janece Flippo: 120; Friedrich Stark: 172; Archive Images: 164; Panther Media GmbH: 216. Art Resource, NY/SCALA/The Museum of Modern Art, NY/ARS, NY, Chagall, Marc, (1887–1985), *Birthday* (*L'Anniversaire*), 1915, oil on canvas 31 3/4 X 39 1/4, acquired through the Lillie P. Bliss Bequest: 125. Alejandro Balaguer: 80–81 *bottom*. Becker Medical Library, Washington University School of Medicine: 145 *bottom*. Bridgeman Images/Romeo and Juliet from 'Children's Stories from Shakespeare' by Edith Nesbit (1858–1924) pub. by Raphael Tuck & Sons Ltd., London (book illustration), Bacon, John Henry Frederick (1868–1914)/Private Collection: 104; Metropolitan Museum of Art, New York, : 64; National Geographic Image Collection: 12–13; Yale Center for British Art, Paul Mellon Collection: 28. Corbis/Blend Images/Hill Street Studios: 128; moodboard/Mike Watson: 20. Digital Vision: 113 *top*. Dreamstime.com/Cosmin Iftode: 60. Fotolia.com/ highwaystarz: 10. Getty Images/ Bettmann: 148, 156, 157 *right*, 204; Corbis: 220; Richard Ellis: 113 *center*, Archive Photos: 188 *right*, Gammo–Rapho/Raphael Gaillarde: 213; Hill Street Studios: 88; Hulton Archive/Central Press: 189 *top*; Keeneland/Bert Morgan: 168 *top*, 169 *bottom*; Rob Lang: 16; Popperfoto: 157 *left*, Sports Illustrated/Jerry Cooke: 169 *top*; Stringer/Oscar Gustav Rejlander: 192; The LIFE Images Collection/Alfred Eisenstaedt: 84; The LIFE Images Collection/Lee Lockwood: 124; Underwood Archives: 37. Granger, NYC: 36 *bottom*, 212. The Image Works/TopFoto: 201 *bottom*. Minden Pictures/Nature Production/Shinji Kusano: 113 *bottom*. New York Public Library Picture Collection/Print Collection, Miriam and Ira D. Wallach Division of Art, Prints and Photographs: 36 *top*. Photodisc: 157 *top*. REX Features Ltd/CBS-TV: 152. Shutterstock.com/3d brained: 188 *left*, Iwona Grodzka: 24–25, 25 *top*; Jean Schweitzer: 168 *bottom*; Joao Virissimo: 24; Kesu: 25 *bottom*; Guenter Albers: 208; Alizada Studios: 176; Everett Historical: 40. St Bartholomew's Hospital Archives & Museum, North Wing, St Bartholomew's Hospital, West Smithfield London, EC1A 7BE/The Royal London Hospital Archives & Museum, The Royal London Hospital, Whitechapel, London, E1 1BB: 69. Superstock/Clover: 213–214; Yoshio Tomi: 81 *top*; age fotostock/David Cole: 32; ClassicStock.com: 196; Culver Pictures, Inc.: 108; Image Asset Management Ltd: 144 *left*, Minden Pictures: 112; Rubberball: 145 *top*. REUTERS/File Photo: 201 *top*. Wikimedia Commons/Contitentalis: 13 *top*; U.S. National Archives and Records Administration: 160; Abbie Rowe (1905–1967): 72; National Portrait Gallery: 132; Royal London Hospital Archives: 68. Wikipedia: 12 *left*, The Library of French Medicine: 144 *right*. World Health Organization: 200.

Illustrator Credits: Lazlo Kubinyi: 100–101. Ron Tanovitz: 56–57.

Address inquiries to Permissions Department,
William H. Sadlier, Inc.,
9 Pine Street, New York, New York 10005-4700.

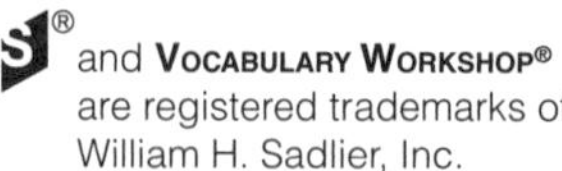

Printed in the United States of America.
ISBN: 978-1-4217-8507-3
2 3 4 5 6 7 8 9 10 EB 21 20 19 18 17

For additional online resources, go to SadlierConnect.com.

CONTENTS

PROGRAM FEATURES

For more than five decades, **Vocabulary Workshop** has proven to be a highly successful tool for vocabulary growth and the development of vocabulary skills. It has also been shown to help students prepare for standardized tests. **Vocabulary Workshop Achieve** maintains that tradition in a newly designed format.

Each of **Vocabulary Workshop Achieve's** 15 Units introduces 20 words in two 10-word lists—**Set A** and **Set B**. Both Set A and Set B contain exercises to help you develop deeper understanding of the 10 words in each set. Combined Sets A and B then provide practice with all 20 of the words in the Unit. Review and Word Study activities follow Units 3, 6, 9, 12, and 15 and offer practice with the 60 vocabulary words in the preceding three Units.

Each level of **Vocabulary Workshop Achieve** introduces and provides practice with 300 vocabulary words and contains features such as reading passages, writing prompts, vocabulary in context, evidence-based questions, and word study that will help you to master these new vocabulary words and succeed in using skills to comprehend unfamiliar words.

Each Unit in **Vocabulary Workshop Achieve** consists of the following sections for **Set A** and **Set B**: an introductory **Reading Passage** that shows how vocabulary words are used in context, **Definitions** that include sentences that give examples of how to use the words, **Using Context, Choosing the Right Word**, and **Completing the Sentence**—activities that provide practice with the vocabulary words. Each introductory **Reading Passage** is a nonfiction text that includes most of the vocabulary words from the Unit to which it belongs. In addition, **Synonyms**, **Antonyms**, and **Vocabulary in Context** in combined Sets A and B round out each Unit with practice with all 20 Unit words.

The five Review sections cover all 60 words from their corresponding Units. **Vocabulary for Comprehension** is modeled on the reading sections of college entrance exams. It presents reading comprehension questions, including vocabulary-related items and evidence-based items that are based on the reading passages.

Word Study sections that contain activities on **Idioms**, **Denotation and Connotation**, and **Classical Roots** follow the Review. These sections will help you develop your understanding of figurative language and practice skills that will help you to determine the meaning of new and unfamiliar vocabulary.

The Final Mastery Test assesses a selection of words from the year and allows you to see the growth you have made in acquiring new vocabulary words and in mastering the comprehension skills you need to understand unfamiliar words.

ONLINE RESOURCES

SadlierConnect.com

Go to **SadlierConnect.com** to find iWords, an audio program that provides pronunciations, definitions, and examples of usage for all of the vocabulary words presented in this level of **Vocabulary Workshop Achieve**. You can listen to the entire **Reading Passage** and the 20 Unit vocabulary words one word at a time, or download all of the words in any given Unit.

At **SadlierConnect.com** you will also find interactive vocabulary quizzes, flash cards, and interactive games and puzzles that will help reinforce and enrich your understanding of the vocabulary words in this level of **Vocabulary Workshop Achieve**.

VOCABULARY IN CONTEXT

The context of a word is the printed text of which that word is part. By studying a word's context, we may find clues to its meaning. We might find a clue in the immediate or adjoining sentence or phrase in which the word appears; in the topic or subject matter of the passage; or in the physical features—such as photographs, illustrations, charts, graphs, captions, and headings—of a page itself.

The **Reading Passages** as well as the **Using Context**, **Choosing the Right Word**, **Vocabulary in Context**, and **Vocabulary for Comprehension** exercises that appear in the Units, the Reviews, and the Final Mastery Test provide practice in using context to decode and to determine the meaning of unfamiliar words.

Three types of context clues appear in the exercises in this book.

A **restatement clue** consists of a synonym for or a definition of the missing word. For example:

Faithfully reading a weekly newsmagazine not only broadens my knowledge of current events and world or national affairs but also ______________ my vocabulary.

a. decreases **b.** fragments **c.** increases **d.** contains

In this sentence, *broadens* is a synonym of the missing word, *increases*, and acts as a restatement clue for it.

A **contrast clue** consists of an antonym for or a phase that means the opposite of the missing word. For example:

"My view of the situation may be far too rosy," I admitted. "On the other hand, yours may be a bit (**optimistic, bleak**)."

In this sentence, *rosy* is an antonym of the missing word, *bleak*. This is confirmed by the presence of the phrase *on the other hand*, which indicates that the answer must be the opposite of *rosy*.

An **inference clue** implies but does not directly state the meaning of the missing word or words. For example:

"A treat for all ages," the review read, "this wonderful novel combines the ______________ of a scholar with the skill and artistry of an expert ______________."

a. ignorance . . . painter **c.** wealth . . . surgeon

b. wisdom . . . beginner **d.** knowledge . . . storyteller

In this sentence, there are several inference clues: (a) the word *scholar* suggests knowledge; (b) the words *novel*, *artistry*, and *skill* suggests the word *storyteller*. These words are inference clues because they suggest or imply, but do not directly state, the missing word or words.

VOCABULARY AND READING

There is a strong connection between vocabulary knowledge and reading comprehension. Although comprehension is much more than recognizing words and knowing their meanings, comprehension is nearly impossible if you do not know an adequate number of words in the text you are reading or have the vocabulary skills to figure out their meaning.

The **Reading Passages** in this level provide extra practice with vocabulary words. Vocabulary words are in boldface to draw your attention to their uses and contexts. Context clues embedded in the passages encourage you to figure out the meanings of words before you read the definitions provided on the pages directly following the passages.

Test Prep

Your knowledge of word meanings and your ability to think carefully about what you read will help you succeed in school and on standards-aligned and state exams.

The **Vocabulary for Comprehension** exercises in each Review consist of a reading passage followed by comprehension questions. The passages and questions are similar to those that you are likely to find on standards-aligned and state exams.

Types of Questions

You are likely to encounter the following types of questions in **Vocabulary Workshop Achieve** and on standards-aligned and state exams.

Main Idea Questions generally ask what the passage as a whole is about. Often, but not always, the main idea is stated in the first paragraph of the passage. You may also be asked the main idea of a specific paragraph. Questions about the main idea may begin like this:

- The primary or main purpose of the passage is . . .
- The author's primary or main purpose in the passage is to . . .
- Which of the following statements most nearly paraphrases the author's main idea in the ninth paragraph (lines 77–88)?
- The main purpose of the fourth paragraph (lines 16–25) is to . . .

Detail Questions focus on important information that is explicitly stated in the passage. Often, however, the correct answer choices do not use the exact language of the passage. They are instead restatements, or paraphrases, of the text.

Vocabulary in Context Questions check your ability to use context to identify a word's meaning. For example:

- As it is used in paragraph 2, "adherents" most nearly means . . .

Use the word's context in a passage to select the best answer, particularly when the vocabulary word has more than one meaning. The answer choices may contain two (or more) correct meanings of the word in question. Choose the meaning that best fits the context.

Inference Questions ask you to make inferences or draw conclusions from the passage. These questions often begin like this:

- It can be most reasonably inferred from the information in the fifth paragraph (lines 53–69) that . . .
- The passage clearly implies that . . .

The inferences you make and the conclusions you draw must be based on the information in the passage. Using the facts you learn from the passage in addition to the knowledge and reasoning you already have helps you understand what is implied and reach conclusions that are logical.

Evidence-Based Questions ask you to provide evidence from the passage that will support the answer you provided to a previous question. These questions often begin like this:

- Which choice provides the best evidence for the answer to the previous question?
- Which statement is the best evidence for the answer to the previous question?

Questions About Tone show your understanding of the author's attitude toward the topic of the passage. To determine the tone, pay attention to the author's word choice. The author's attitude may be positive (respectful), negative (scornful), or neutral (distant). These are typical questions:

- The author's primary purpose in the passage is to . . .
- Which word best describes the author's tone?

Questions About Author's Technique focus on the way a text is organized and the language the author uses. These questions ask you to think about structure and function. For example:

- In the context of the passage, the primary function of the fourth paragraph (lines 30–37) is to . . .
- The organizational structure of the passage is best described as . . .

To answer the questions, you must demonstrate an understanding of the way the author presents information and develops ideas.

VOCABULARY AND WRITING

The **Writing: Words in Action** prompt provides you with an opportunity to practice using text evidence to respond to a prompt about the introductory **Reading Passage**. You will have the opportunity to demonstrate your understanding of the Unit words by incorporating the new vocabulary you have learned into your own writing.

WORD STUDY

Word Study helps build word knowledge with strategies to help you look closely at words for meanings. Word Study instruction and practice include **Idioms**, **Denotation and Connotation**, and **Classical Roots**.

Idioms

Three Word Study sections feature instruction on and practice with idioms. An idiom is an informal expression whose literal meaning does not help the reader or listener understand what the expression means, such as "raining cats and dogs," "the apple of my eye," or "a dark horse." While every language has its own idioms, English is particularly rich in idioms and idiomatic expressions. Developing a clear understanding of idioms will help you better understand the figurative language that authors use in their writing.

Denotation and Connotation

Instruction in **Denotation and Connotation** and practice with connotations is included in two of the Word Study sections. Understanding a word's connotation will develop your skills as a reader, writer, and speaker.

Understanding the difference between denotation and connotation is important to understanding definitions and how concepts are used, as well as in choosing the right word. In these exercises, practice choosing the correct word by determining the emotional association of the word.

Classical Roots

Each Word Study includes a **Classical Roots** exercise that provides instruction in and practice with Greek and Latin roots. Developing a useful, transferable technique to make sense out of unfamiliar words through Greek and Latin roots will help you unlock the meanings of thousands of words. An example word drawn from the vocabulary words in the previous Units is referenced at the top of the page and serves as a guide to help you complete the exercise.

PRONUNCIATION KEY

The pronunciation is indicated for every basic word in this book. The pronunciation symbols used are similar to those used in most recent standard dictionaries. The author has primarily consulted *Webster's Third New International Dictionary* and *The Random House Dictionary of the English Language* (*Unabridged*). Many English words have multiple accepted pronunciations. The author has given one pronunciation when such words occur in this book except when the pronunciation changes according to the part of speech. For example, the verb *project* is pronounced **prə jekt'**, and the noun form is pronounced **präj' ekt**.

Vowels	ā	l*a*ke	e	str*e*ss	ü	l*oo*t, n*ew*
	a	m*a*t	ī	kn*i*fe	u̇	f*oo*t, p*u*ll
	â	c*a*re	i	s*i*t	ə	j*u*mp, brok*e*n
	ä	b*a*rk, b*o*ttle	ō	fl*ow*	ər	b*ir*d, bett*er*
	au̇	d*ou*bt	ô	*a*ll, c*o*rd		
	ē	b*ea*t, word*y*	oi	*oi*l		

Consonants	ch	*ch*ild, lec*t*ure	s	*c*ellar	wh	*wh*at
	g	*g*ive	sh	*sh*un	y	*y*earn
	j	*g*entle, bri*dg*e	th	*th*ank	z	i*s*
	ŋ	si*ng*	t̶h̶	*th*ose	zh	mea*s*ure

All other consonants are sounded as in the alphabet.

Stress The accent mark follows the syllable receiving the major stress: en rich'.

Abbreviations	*adj.*	adjective	*n.*	noun	*prep.*	preposition
	adv.	adverb	*part.*	participle	*v.*	verb
	int.	interjection	*pl.*	plural		

Read the following passage, taking note of the ***boldface*** *words and their contexts. These words are among those you will be studying in Unit 1. It may help you to complete the exercises in this Unit if you refer to the way the words are used below.*

The Times of Zheng He

<Narrative Nonfiction>

Zheng He was born in the year 1371, in the Chinese province of Yunnan. He was descended from a Persian who had been governor of Yunnan over a century before, in the early days of the Mongol-led Yuan **Dynasty**. The family retained its connections to the Mongol rulers of China through those years. But nothing is **interminable** in this world. A change was in the wind. About the time Zheng was born, the Ming clan asserted itself as the new ruling dynasty in China. Ming armies pushed the Mongols out of China and back to their homeland in Mongolia, an **adjacent** country in the north, dry and rather **barren**.

Emperor Zhu Di of the Ming Dynasty

While Zheng was still a boy, pockets of Mongol loyalists remained in certain areas of China, not least in the southern province of Yunnan. Unrest erupted wherever loyalists lived. Zheng was about ten years old when political turmoil **disrupted** his life, forever altering its course. His father was killed in 1381 during the Ming army's conquest of Yunnan. Zheng was captured and sent to the court of Prince Zhu Di, son of the Ming emperor. If the boy was **sullen** and withdrawn at first, he did not remain so for long. He became one of the prince's trusted advisors, gradually **insinuating** himself into a position of respect. In time, Prince Zhu Di sought to depose his own nephew, who had become the second Ming emperor. When the hour came, he relied on Zheng's assistance. And when the insurrection proved successful, Zhu Di had become the third Ming emperor of China, and Zheng He was now the right hand to the emperor.

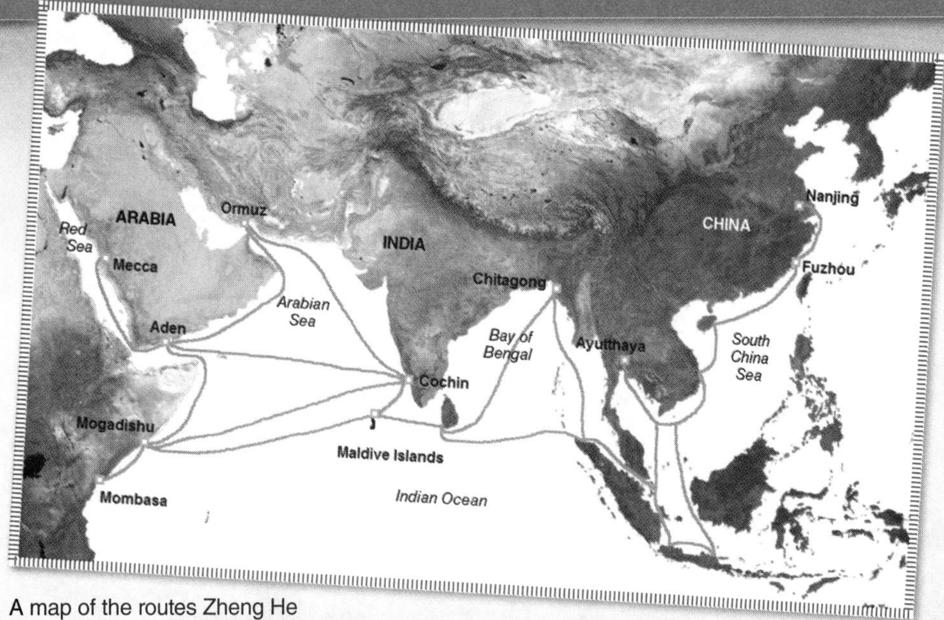

A map of the routes Zheng He took during his expeditions

This adventure was only a **foretaste** of what lay ahead for Zheng He. The new emperor had ambitious plans to **renovate** China after years of **vicious** war had reduced the population and stalled production to a **trickle**. The emperor planned to restore the economy, promote construction, maintain order and protect the borders, stimulate culture and learning, and extend China's influence throughout the world. As part of his vision, he sponsored a series of massive naval expeditions, appointing Zheng to be chief envoy and leader of the fleet.

Zheng led six expeditions for the emperor, his own prestige increasing with each notch in his **résumé**. The first expedition set off in 1405, with about 300 huge ships and nearly 30,000 men. At the time, it was the largest fleet ever to have sailed from China. The main purpose of the expeditions was not exploration, or conquest, or commerce, but diplomacy. Zheng's giant fleet and the soldiers who manned it made a strong impression wherever they went. They projected an image of Chinese wealth and power. The troops were rarely called on for a display of force; the size of the fleet was intimidating enough. Wherever Zheng **alighted**, he had an opportunity to **interrogate** the locals for news, meet with local elites to exchange gifts and information, and represent the interests of the Chinese emperor.

The emperor died in 1424. His successors did not continue his maritime policy. Zheng He led one more fleet in 1433. He died during this last great expedition and was buried at sea. Seeds of foreign relations planted during his lifetime **germinated** even after he was gone.

The Hall of Supreme Harmony, one of China's greatest buildings, was built in 1406 for the Ming emperor Zhu Di.

Audio

For iWords and audio passages, go to **SadlierConnect.com**.

Definitions

Note the spelling, pronunciation, part(s) of speech, and definition(s) of each of the following words. Then write the appropriate form of the word in the blank space in the illustrative sentence(s) following.

1. alight (ə līt′) — (*v.*) to get down from, step down from; to come down from the air, land; (*adj.*) lighted up

The passengers hurried to ________________ from the small airplane.

The sky was ________________ with a red glow as the fire raged in the distance.

2. dynasty (dī′ nə stē) — (*n.*) a powerful family or group of rulers that maintains its position or power for some time

The Han ________________ of China was in power for about 400 years.

3. germinate (jər′ mə nāt) — (*v.*) to begin to grow, come into being

After he interrogated the suspect, suspicion began to ________________ in the inspector's mind.

4. humdrum (həm′ drəm) — (*adj.*) ordinary, dull, routine, without variation

All household tasks are ________________, according to my brother, who never helps with them.

5. insinuate (in sin′ yü āt) — (*v.*) to suggest or hint slyly; to edge into something indirectly

The attorney attempted to ________________ that the witness's testimony was false.

6. interrogate (in ter′ ə gāt) — (*v.*) to ask questions, examine by questioning

Two detectives helped the young, inexperienced officer to ________________ the suspect.

7. résumé (rez′ ə mā) — (*n.*) a brief summary; a short written account of one's education, working experience, or qualifications for a job

The job applicant gave a copy of her ________________ to the person in charge of the employment agency.

8. trivial (triv′ ē əl) — (*adj.*) not important, minor; ordinary, commonplace

The general left all ________________ details to subordinate officers.

9. truce (trüs)
(*n.*) a pause in fighting, temporary peace
After tense negotiations, the warring nations reluctantly agreed to a five-day ____________.

10. vicious (vish′ əs)
(*adj.*) evil, bad; spiteful; having bad habits or an ugly disposition; painfully severe or extreme
The ____________ rumor was damaging to their budding friendship.

For each item, determine whether the ***boldface*** *word from pages 14–15 makes sense in the context of the sentence. Circle the item numbers next to the six sentences in which the words are used correctly.*

1. Animals that are usually harmless can become **vicious** if they feel they are being threatened.
2. In the evening hours, the city's theater district is filled with bright lights and **humdrum** activity.
3. The servants arranged themselves in a long single row and waited for the new owner of the estate to **alight** from his carriage so they could formally greet him.
4. In addition to proofreading your **résumé** yourself, you should ask someone else to read it over as well to make sure it is free of obvious errors.
5. The leader was celebrated for being a **dynasty** because of the short amount of time she ruled over the people.
6. Ideas often **germinate** when you least expect them to.
7. This bulldozer can **interrogate** that pile of earth and rocks in just a few minutes.
8. After more than 20 years of fighting, the feuding kingdoms grew weary and finally agreed to a **truce**.
9. The two plans for merging the film studios are basically the same; any differences between them are **trivial**.
10. Because the organization's budget is tight, its managers will have to find ways to **insinuate** existing resources.

Choosing the Right Word

*Select the **boldface** word that better completes each sentence. You might refer to the passage on pages 12–13 to see how most of these words are used in context. Note that the choices might be related forms of the Unit words.*

1. I'd been looking forward to the new TV series on Monday nights, but the first episode turned out to be just another (**humdrum, vicious**) detective story.

2. "The program the usher handed you contains a brief (**résumé, dynasty**) of the action of the opera you are about to see," I replied.

3. He said that he was going to ask only "a few casual questions," but I soon saw that he wanted to (**germinate, interrogate**) me thoroughly.

4. Planted in the fertile soil of her imagination, the seed of a great idea soon (**germinated, alighted**) into a workable proposal.

5. Even the most (**humdrum, vicious**) work can be interesting if you regard it as a challenge to do the very best you can.

6. Regardless of who started this silly quarrel, isn't it time for us to declare a (**dynasty, truce**) and work together for the best interests of the school?

7. The way to be successful at a job is to carry out all instructions carefully, even though you think some of them are (**trivial, humdrum**) or silly.

8. For three generations, their family has formed one of the leading automotive (**truces, dynasties**) of this country.

9. With flattery and clever half-truths, the newcomers (**insinuated, interrogated**) themselves into the inner circle of the organization.

10. I am angry not because she criticized me but because she made remarks that were untrue and (**trivial, vicious**).

11. The flight attendant asked the passengers to make sure that they had all their personal belongings before (**insinuating, alighting**) from the aircraft.

12. Representatives from both nations met to negotiate a (**dynasty, truce**) to give each side a chance to care for its wounded.

Completing the Sentence

Choose the word from the word bank that best completes each of the following sentences. Write the correct word or form of the word in the space provided.

alight	**germinate**	**insinuate**	**résumé**	**truce**
dynasty	**humdrum**	**interrogate**	**trivial**	**vicious**

1. In the eleventh century, a foreign warlord invaded the country and set up a(n) ________________ that ruled for more than 250 years.
2. When I applied for the job, I left a(n) ________________ of my previous work experience with the personnel office.
3. After the warring nations had agreed to a(n) ________________, they faced the far more difficult task of working out a real peace.
4. Though they didn't say it in so many words, they did ________________ that I was responsible for the accident.
5. As we sat at the side of the lake, we enjoyed watching the wild geese swoop down and ________________ on the surface of the water.
6. The judge said to the lawyer, "You have a right to ________________ the witness, but there is no need to bully her."
7. I never would have thought that so bitter and long-lasting a quarrel could result from such a(n) ________________ and unimportant cause.
8. In only a few days, the seeds that I had planted in the fertile soil of the garden began to ________________ and take root.
9. Many people who lead rather ________________ lives get a great thrill from watching the exciting adventures of TV and movie superheroes.
10. Though my dog, Rover, is huge and fierce-looking, children are fond of him because he doesn't have a(n) ________________ disposition.

Definitions

Note the spelling, pronunciation, part(s) of speech, and definition(s) of each of the following words. Then write the appropriate form of the word in the blank space in the illustrative sentence(s) following.

1. adjacent (ə jās′ ənt)
(*adj.*) near, next to, adjoining
Boston and its ________________ suburbs were severely flooded after three days of heavy rain.

2. barren (bar′ ən)
(*adj.*) not productive, bare
In contrast to the rich land we left behind, the plains appeared to be a ________________ landscape.

3. disrupt (dis rəpt′)
(*v.*) to break up, disturb
Even the loud demonstration on the street below was not enough to ________________ the meeting.

4. foretaste (fôr′ tāst)
(*n.*) an advance indication, sample, or warning
The eye-opening first scene of the new play gave the audience a ________________ of things to come.

5. hurtle (hər′ təl)
(*v.*) to rush violently, dash headlong; to fling or hurl forcefully
After separating from its booster rocket, the capsule began to ________________ through space.

6. interminable (in tər′ mə nə bəl)
(*adj.*) endless, so long as to seem endless
We had an ________________ wait in the hot, crowded train station.

7. recompense (rek′ əm pens)
(*v.*) to pay back; to give a reward; (*n.*) a payment for loss, service, or injury
My grandparents were happy to ________________ the little girl who found their lost puppy.
As ________________, the landlord offered all tenants a month free of rent.

8. renovate (ren′ ə vāt)
(*v.*) to repair, restore to good condition, make new again
The young couple brought in an architect and a contractor to help them ________________ the old house.

9. sullen (səl′ ən)
(*adj.*) silent or brooding because of ill humor, anger, or resentment; slow moving, sluggish

The _________________ student sat down in the back of the classroom.

10. trickle (trik′ əl)
(*v.*) to flow or fall by drops or in a small stream; (*n.*) a small, irregular quantity of anything

The water began to _________________ from the rusty old pipe.

The runoff, which is quite heavy in the spring, dwindles to a _________________ by late summer.

Using Context

*For each item, determine whether the **boldface** word from pages 18–19 makes sense in the context of the sentence. Circle the item numbers next to the six sentences in which the words are used correctly.*

1. It is so hot outside that sweat begins to **trickle** down my forehead as soon as I step outside.
2. His worst quality is his tendency to **recompense** the thoughts of others and pass them off as his own.
3. The light drizzle was just a **foretaste** of the rain that would bombard our city for the next two weeks.
4. Nothing can **disrupt** a good class discussion more abruptly than the clanging bells of a fire drill.
5. I find nothing more thrilling than being on a roller coaster and feeling the wind in my face as we **hurtle** around the track.
6. Even though the two houses are **adjacent** to each other, they look as if they belong in completely different neighborhoods.
7. Her sense of humor is so **sullen** that some people don't realize she's joking, though I appreciate her understated approach.
8. It's a pleasure to work with someone who has such a **barren** mind and can come up with creative solutions to every problem.
9. No matter how hard I tried, I could not **renovate** the feeling that something unfortunate was about to happen.
10. As we sat in seemingly **interminable** traffic, I wondered if this road trip was worth so much lost time spent in the car.

*Select the **boldface** word that better completes each sentence. You might refer to the passage on pages 12–13 to see how most of these words are used in context. Note that the choices might be related forms of the Unit words.*

1. Our team spirit is so high that there is never a (**sullen, barren**) reaction from players who aren't chosen to start a game.

2. If the sights we've seen today are a true (**recompense, foretaste**) of what lies ahead, we're in for some real treats.

3. Only twenty yards from the finish line, the horse stumbled and (**hurtled, disrupted**) its rider to the ground.

4. The principal asked the students not to hang around in front of the houses and other buildings (**adjacent to, barren to**) the school.

5. What we want to do is (**recompense, renovate**) the old house without harming its charm and beauty.

6. When I saw a big "A" on my term paper in English, I felt that I had been fully (**disrupted, recompensed**) for all my hours of hard work.

7. The administration had no major scandals, but it was also (**barren, sullen**) of outstanding accomplishments.

8. As he grew old, the torrent of beautiful music that he had produced for so many years was reduced to a mere (**foretaste, trickle**).

9. What would you consider an adequate (**foretaste, recompense**) for having worked so many extra hours on the job?

10. Sometime in mid-August, you can view the spectacular Perseid meteor shower, as comet debris (**hurtle, renovate**) through space and enter Earth's atmosphere.

11. Are we going to allow minor disagreements to (**disrupt, recompense**) the club that we have worked so hard to organize?

12. When we are having fun, time rushes by, but even five minutes in the dentist's waiting room may seem (**adjacent, interminable**).

Choose the word from the word bank that best completes each of the following sentences. Write the correct word or form of the word in the space provided.

adjacent	**disrupt**	**hurtle**	**recompense**	**sullen**
barren	**foretaste**	**interminable**	**renovate**	**trickle**

1. Our carefully laid plans were completely ______________ by a sudden and totally unexpected turn of events.

2. During the exciting chase, the police cars ______________ through the town.

3. The "coming attractions" shown before the main feature gave us a distinct ______________ of what the next film would be like.

4. Although the building is old and needs repair, we are convinced that we can ______________ it without spending a lot of money.

5. She was so happy and grateful that I felt more than ______________ for all that I had tried to do to help her.

6. The suspect's only reaction to the detective's question was a wry smile and ______________ silence.

7. Although they lived in a house ______________ to ours, we never really got to know them well.

8. As the drought continued without a letup, the once fertile farmlands of the region slowly became ______________ "dust bowls."

9. We need large sums of money to keep our school system going, but we are getting only a(n) ______________ of funds from the state.

10. After the big party, cleaning up, which was supposed to take "just a few minutes," proved to be an almost ______________ job.

Synonyms

*Choose the word or form of the word from this Unit that is the same or most nearly the same in meaning as the **boldface** word or expression in the phrase. Write that word on the line. Use a dictionary if necessary.*

1. to **reimburse** her expenses _______________
2. sent a **job history** to the company _______________
3. bare and **unproductive** cornfields _______________
4. told a **never-ending** tale of woe _______________
5. a **preview** of what is to come _______________
6. received information in **dribbles** _______________
7. as the **ruling house** came to the end of its reign _______________
8. sat and stared with a **grumpy** pout _______________
9. **question** the witness _______________
10. decided to **fix up** the old theater _______________
11. his attempt to **descend** from the plane _______________
12. the **development** of a plan _______________
13. **intimate** that it was her fault _______________
14. travel plans **interrupted** by her illness _______________
15. chased by the **savage** bear _______________

Antonyms

*Choose the word or form of the word from this Unit that is most nearly opposite in meaning to the **boldface** word or expression in the phrase. Write that word on the line. Use a dictionary if necessary.*

1. definitely a **momentous** decision _______________
2. hope to continue their **battle** _______________
3. moved to a **faraway** town _______________
4. to **move slowly** down the narrow path _______________
5. leads a **lively** existence _______________

Writing: Words in Action

Imagine that you are Zheng He near the end of his life. What do you think are your greatest accomplishments? How would you like to be remembered? Write a journal entry, using at least two details from the passage (pages 12–13) and three or more words from this Unit.

Vocabulary in Context

*Some of the words you have studied in this Unit appear in **boldface** type. Read the passage below, and then circle the letter of the correct answer for each word as it is used in context.*

Let's **hurtle** back through time to the beginning of ancient Chinese architecture. Much of traditional Chinese architecture made use of timber, and had buildings with tile roofs. Over time, stone carvings, rammed-earth construction, bucket arch buildings, and other techniques became part of the style of ancient Chinese architecture.

In the sixteenth century BCE, the Shang **dynasty** in China established two main design ideas of ancient Chinese architecture. The first design idea was that buildings should be long and low, with roofs held up by columns rather than walls. The roofs should appear to float above the ground. The second design idea emphasized symmetry. Symmetry meant that both sides of the building should be in balance. While this aspect of design may seem **trivial**, symmetry and balance are central to Taoism.

Fast forward to 221 BCE and the advent of Chinese imperial architecture. E'Pang Palace and Weiyang Palace were designed so that the royal family could live in one area while the emperor could conduct public affairs, such as negotiating a **truce**, in another area. Some of the sullen laborers of these ancient buildings were enslaved, and thus, they did not receive **recompense** for their work.

Ancient Chinese architecture, with its unique features that are far from **humdrum**, has made significant contributions to the world architectural system. Aspects of ancient Chinese architecture are visible in modern marvels like the Great Wall and the Forbidden City. Modern China owes a debt of gratitude to its beautiful ancient architecture.

---

1. The word **hurtle** means about the same as

a. reverse **c.** speed
b. lift **d.** shift

2. **Dynasty** comes from the Greek word **dunastēs**. **Dunastēs** most likely means

a. lord **c.** author
b. worker **d.** chef

3. Which word means the same as **trivial** as it is used in paragraph 2?

a. minor **c.** expensive
b. elaborate **d.** questionable

4. What is the meaning of **truce** as it is used in paragraph 3?

a. crucial agreement **c.** lengthy amendment
b. permanent treaty **d.** temporary peace

5. What is the meaning of **recompense** as it is used in paragraph 3?

a. benefits **c.** credit
b. payment **d.** respite

6. Which word means the opposite of **humdrum** as it is used in paragraph 4?

a. ordinary **c.** artistic
b. distinctive **d.** exciting

UNIT 2

*Read the following passage, taking note of the **boldface** words and their contexts. These words are among those you will be studying in Unit 2. It may help you to complete the exercises in this Unit if you refer to the way the words are used below.*

In Poor Taste

<Letter to the Editor>

To the Editor:
RE: "Fast-Food Ads Target Kids"
(*Business section, October 29*)

Our children are sitting ducks in an advertising war. The "combatants" are the food and beverage companies, advertising agencies, and media corporations **pelting** kids with a dangerous diet of junk food and soft drink ads.

I am no troublesome **firebrand**. I am a nurse at a middle school. I am also the mother of three school-age children. I am writing to express my **indignation** and frustration at the **indifference** of those trying to get one over on the public and, specifically, our kids.

Turn on any children's TV show or visit a website that **caters** to kids. You'll be bombarded with cute characters proclaiming how cool it is to eat Brand "X" cereal or Brand "Y" convenience food. Web sites are full of banner ads and interactive games with commercial content. The problem is, most young children don't have the sophistication to understand the power of persuasive commercials. They think if their favorite animated dragon says eating sugar-laden gooey treats is good for you, it must be so.

According to the Centers for Disease Control and Prevention, childhood obesity in the United States has nearly tripled in the past 30 years. Being significantly overweight is a dangerous health **hazard**. Plus, rates for both diabetes and asthma are soaring. Experts say the rise in both is linked to the rise in childhood obesity. Good health is **indispensable** for a long and happy life. Our youngest generation is **poised** to become the unhealthiest in history.

Despite these alarming facts, the food industry and their advertisers use every **available** media outlet to promote and sell their products. Although their marketing techniques don't break any laws, pushing food and drinks low in nutritional value and high in sugar, salt, and fat is unethical. Instead of encouraging kids to make good food choices, most of these companies use misleading tactics that **hinder** healthy eating goals. In fact, a recent university study found that, on any given day, one-third of American children and teens eat fast food.

In an ideal world, I'd like all food advertisements aimed at kids banned from children's programming. But I know that's not realistic. After all, we're talking about a multibillion-dollar industry. So I demand that companies involved in the making, marketing, and selling of food be required to be far more **transparent** in their advertising to children. I also demand that regulating agencies such as the Federal Trade Commission set far tougher policies. It's painfully clear that self-regulating guidelines for the food industry are not working.

As a nurse and mom, it is **customary** for me to be concerned about the health of kids. I will keep doing all I can to **dissuade** them from choosing junk food over healthy food. I will also continue to **plague** junk-food peddlers and the government officials who **mutually** benefit from leaving things as they are.

Human beings are, after all, just human. We'll always have our bad habits. But cigarette advertising has been banned from the airwaves. Alcohol advertising is strictly regulated. So why do we allow advertising for junk food?

K. D. Nettles, R.N.
Yarmouth, Maine

Audio

For iWords and audio passages, go to **SadlierConnect.com**.

Definitions

Note the spelling, pronunciation, part(s) of speech, and definition(s) of each of the following words. Then write the appropriate form of the word in the blank space in the illustrative sentence(s) following.

1. cater (kā′ tər) — (*v.*) to satisfy the needs of, try to make things easy and pleasant; to supply food and service

Our grandmother cared for the twins all summer, but she refused to ________ to their every whim.

2. entrepreneur (än trə prə nər′) — (*n.*) a person who starts up and takes on the risk of a business

In the first year of business, an ________ often assumes losses for the sake of future profits.

3. hazard (haz′ ərd) — (*n.*) risk, peril; (*v.*) to expose to danger or harm; to gamble

Snow tires can help eliminate the ________ of driving on icy roads.

When asked to predict when the long drought would end, the meteorologist would not ________ a guess.

4. homicide (hom′ ə sīd) — (*n.*) the killing of one person by another

The jury found the drifter guilty of ________.

5. indignant (in dig′ nənt) — (*adj.*) filled with resentment or anger over something unjust, unworthy, or mean

Angered by the editorial in the newspaper, my mother wrote an ________ letter to the editor.

6. lubricate (lü′ brə kāt) — (*v.*) to apply oil or grease; to make smooth, slippery, or easier to use

The workers had to ________ the equipment regularly so that production would not suffer.

7. mutual (myü′ chü əl) — (*adj.*) shared, felt, or shown equally by two or more

During the course of the summer, the adoring couple formed a ________ admiration society.

8. plague (plāg) — (*n.*) an easily spread disease causing a large number of deaths; a widespread evil; (*v.*) to annoy or bother

In the fourteenth century, a ________ wiped out about one-fourth of the population of Europe.

Mosquitoes will ________ the campers if they forget to wear insect repellent on the hike.

9. transparent (trans par′ ənt)
(*adj.*) allowing light to pass through; easily recognized or understood; easily seen through or detected
The students could see the other class through the ________________ glass door.

10. unscathed (ən skathd′)
(*adj.*) wholly unharmed, not injured
Remarkably, the captain and the entire crew emerged from the wreck ________________.

Using Context

For each item, determine whether the ***boldface*** *word from pages 26–27 makes sense in the context of the sentence. Circle the item numbers next to the six sentences in which the words are used correctly.*

1. When people childproof a home, they identify and remove every possible **hazard**, such as an exposed electrical wire or outlet.

2. The **entrepreneur** went to a famous acting school because he wanted to be the best at his craft.

3. A police detective was assigned to the case after the death was determined to be a **homicide** rather than an accident.

4. We looked for the perfect gift to thank our hosts for being so **indignant** with us during our two-week stay.

5. The young chef is eager for the opportunity to **cater** the world-famous museum's annual banquet.

6. The **mutual** barking of the dog next door was becoming so annoying that we had to call our neighbors and complain.

7. The jury, completely **unscathed** by the prosecutor's case, quickly returned a verdict of "not guilty."

8. What precautions can public health care officials and ordinary citizens take to prevent the outbreak of a **plague**?

9. If you use a bit of oil to **lubricate** the hinge, the door will stop squeaking every time it is opened.

10. An unusual species known as the glass frog has a body so **transparent** that you can see its heart and other internal organs through its skin.

Choosing the Right Word

*Select the **boldface** word that better completes each sentence. You might refer to the passage on pages 24–25 to see how most of these words are used in context. Note that the choices might be related forms of the Unit words.*

1. In Shakespeare's *Macbeth*, after the (**homicide, entrepreneur**) of the Scottish King Duncan, the sleepwalking Lady Macbeth cries that she cannot clean her bloodstained hands.

2. The aid that we have (**indignantly, mutually**) given each other during the years has enabled both of us to overcome many problems.

3. When the salesclerk replied rudely to my polite inquiry about the price of the garment, I became a bit (**transparent, indignant**).

4. Though I have no means of knowing for sure where Joe and Miguel happen to be, may I (**hazard, lubricate**) the guess that they're in the gym?

5. The judge explained to the jury that killing someone in self-defense may be considered justifiable, or noncriminal, (**homicide, hazard**).

6. A little courtesy can do much to (**hazard, lubricate**) the machinery of our everyday social life.

7. Young (**entrepreneurs, plagues**) have made millions from start-up companies that develop and sell apps for smartphones and tablets.

8. Innocent or guilty, no one involved in a major political scandal ever comes away from it entirely (**indignant, unscathed**).

9. All during that nightmarish period, I found myself (**plagued, catered**) by fears about the future.

10. The fire that started from smoldering embers in the chimney totally destroyed the house, but fortunately everyone in the family escaped (**unscathed, indignant**).

11. Do you agree with the criticism that many television programs shamelessly (**cater, lubricate**) to the lowest tastes?

12. Your excuse for missing practice was so (**transparent, unscathed**) that even a child would have seen right through it.

Choose the word from the word bank that best completes each of the following sentences. Write the correct word or form of the word in the space provided.

cater	**hazard**	**indignant**	**mutual**	**transparent**
entrepreneur	**homicide**	**lubricate**	**plague**	**unscathed**

1. When we ____________________ the engine of a car, we try to cut down the friction at every point.

2. Because the seat covers in the car were ____________________, we could see the attractive pattern of the upholstery underneath.

3. When the wounded shopkeeper died, the charges against the person who had been arrested were raised from robbery to ____________________.

4. With the emergence of market economies in Eastern Europe have come hordes of ____________________ seeking business opportunities there.

5. Mother prepares wholesome and tasty meals, but she says she is not going to ____________________ to the special tastes of six different children.

6. No one has ever been able to explain to my satisfaction how any person can walk ____________________ across beds of hot coals.

7. It takes a special kind of bravery to face the ____________________ of life in the jungle.

8. At the front desk, a(n) ____________________ guest was angrily complaining about the shabby treatment he had received from the staff of the hotel.

9. Having spent many years as political opponents, the two senators have since developed a(n) ____________________ respect for each other.

10. Most of the homeowners in this area have tried in vain to overcome the ____________________ of crabgrass that threatens to overrun their lawns.

End Set A

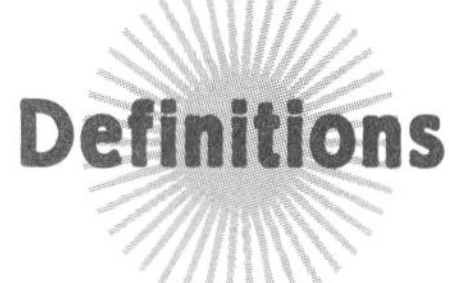

Note the spelling, pronunciation, part(s) of speech, and definition(s) of each of the following words. Then write the appropriate form of the word in the blank space in the illustrative sentence(s) following.

1. available (ə vā′ lə bəl)
(*adj.*) ready for use, at hand
Bean sprouts and bean curd are ____________________ in the Chinese market on Main Street.

2. customary (kəs′ tə mer ē)
(*adj.*) usual, expected, routine
The ____________________ tip given to a waiter for service is 15–20 percent of the bill.

3. dissuade (dis wād′)
(*v.*) to persuade not to do something
Despite offering big raises and bonuses, the boss was unable to ____________________ workers from quitting.

4. firebrand (fī′ ər brand)
(*n.*) a piece of burning wood; a troublemaker; an extremely energetic or emotional person
A rash young ____________________, the new editor of the newspaper strove to expose corruption in the mayor's office.

5. hinder (hin′ dər)
(*v.*) to delay; to stop or prevent from happening
The all-day rain predicted for tomorrow will definitely ____________________ our plans for a picnic at the lake.

6. indifference (in dif′ rəns)
(*n.*) a lack of interest or concern
The outcome of the rugby match between the two teams is a matter of complete ____________________ to me.

7. indispensable (in di spen′ sə bəl)
(*adj.*) absolutely necessary, not to be neglected
Oxygen is a gas that is ____________________ to life processes on this planet.

8. pelt (pelt)
(*v.*) to throw a stream of things; to strike successively; to hurry
The children resisted the urge to ____________________ the cars with snowballs.

9. poised (poizd) — (*adj., part.*) balanced, suspended; calm, controlled; ready for action

The captain and other members of the crew were ______________ for takeoff.

10. regime (rā zhēm′) — (*n.*) a government in power; a form or system of rule or management; a period of rule

The present ______________ in that country came to power through democratic elections.

Using Context

*For each item, determine whether the **boldface** word from pages 30–31 makes sense in the context of the sentence. Circle the item numbers next to the six sentences in which the words are used correctly.*

1. The **indifference** between my dog and my friend's cat is so great that we can never allow them to be in the same room together.
2. He is known throughout the neighborhood as a mysterious **firebrand** who prefers to keep to himself.
3. I was so **poised** before giving my speech that my hands were shaking and my face was bright red.
4. When the interviewer offered me the job, I told him that I was **available** to start working immediately.
5. Nothing seems to **hinder** my ability to exercise more than not getting a good night's sleep.
6. The tale of brave citizens who overthrew an oppressive **regime** to replace it with an ethical government inspired me to stand up for what I believe in.
7. My sister is such a determined young woman that nothing can **dissuade** her from doing something once she has made up her mind.
8. Rather than **pelt** me with petty insults, why don't you explain what is bothering you so that we can have a productive conversation.
9. The Internet seems so **indispensable** to me that I can't imagine how people survived without it for so long.
10. He took only a **customary** glance at the bill when it arrived and did not realize that he had been charged for his meal twice.

Choosing the Right Word

*Select the **boldface** word that better completes each sentence. You might refer to the passage on pages 24–25 to see how most of these words are used in context. Note that the choices might be related forms of the Unit words.*

1. Queen Victoria began her (**firebrand, regime**) in 1837 at the age of 18 and ruled until her death in 1901, a period known as the "Victorian Age."

2. It seems that only last year she was an awkward child, but now she is a charming and (**poised, customary**) young woman.

3. In Shakespeare's day, an actor who displeased the audience might find himself (**hindered, pelted**) with a barrage of rotten vegetables.

4. You cannot ignore me for months on end and then take it for granted that I will be (**available, customary**) whenever you want me.

5. On our long camping trip, we learned that we could get along without many things that we had considered (**indispensable, indifferent**).

6. Southern (**firebrands, dissuaders**) agitating for a complete break with the Union helped speed the coming of the Civil War.

7. When the new (**firebrand, regime**) took power, it canceled or reversed most of the policies of its predecessor.

8. The public's (**indifference, availability**) to government may be measured by the number of people who don't vote.

9. Because I am a creature of habit, I can't do anything in the morning without first having my (**customary, available**) cup of coffee.

10. Antibiotics can be a very effective means of (**pelting, hindering**) the spread of some diseases.

11. Unfortunately, nothing any of us said could (**dissuade, pelt**) Ned from his plan to quit his job.

12. The gymnast was (**poised, indispensable**) atop the balance beam, ready for the most challenging part of the competition.

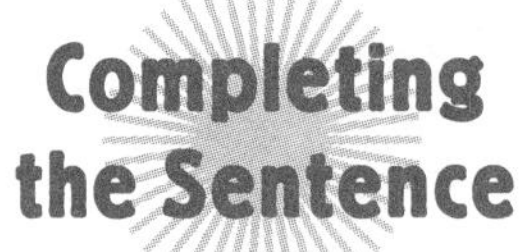

Completing the Sentence

Choose the word from the word bank that best completes each of the following sentences. Write the correct word or form of the word in the space provided.

available	**dissuade**	**hinder**	**indispensable**	**poised**
customary	**firebrand**	**indifference**	**pelt**	**regime**

1. Angry at the call, the crowd began to ____________________ the referee with all kinds of refuse.

2. Until it was almost too late, the hunters did not see the leopard crouching in a tree, ____________________ to leap on them.

3. It took the authorities quite some time to put down the riot that a few rash ____________________ had managed to start.

4. Eventually, the army toppled the country's democratic ____________________ and set up a military dictatorship in its place.

5. A sense of humor is ____________________ if you are to cope with all the strains and difficulties of everyday life.

6. Although the legislators have done nothing to further the passage of the bill, they haven't tried to ____________________ the process either.

7. Although we arrived at the stadium only a few minutes before the game, we found that many good seats were still ____________________.

8. The guidance counselor tried to ____________________ me from taking the job because she thought the work would be too high-pressure for me.

9. Though the habit of taking a siesta in the afternoon may seem strange to a foreigner, it is quite ____________________ in this part of the world.

10. Only a really hard-hearted person could show such ____________________ to the plight of the homeless who wander our streets.

End Set B

Synonyms

*Choose the word or form of the word from this Unit that is the same or most nearly the same in meaning as the **boldface** word or expression in the phrase. Write that word on the line. Use a dictionary if necessary.*

1. began to **pepper** the windshield with hailstones ______
2. hired to **provide** food for the wedding guests ______
3. wants to **discourage** her from taking the job ______
4. is **vital** to the good of the community ______
5. not **obtainable** in my size ______
6. **hamper** the advance of the troops ______
7. had a **shared** understanding ______
8. **lack of concern** about the election ______
9. **ready** to jump at the bell ______
10. the **danger** of walking along the ledge ______
11. found guilty of **murder** ______
12. thrived under the new **administration** ______
13. a swarm of bees that **pestered** the hikers ______
14. is considered a **rabble-rouser** by colleagues ______
15. met the new **impresario** of sports entertainment ______

Antonyms

*Choose the word or form of the word from this Unit that is most nearly opposite in meaning to the **boldface** word or expression in the phrase. Write that word on the line. Use a dictionary if necessary.*

1. was **wounded** in the explosion ______
2. an arid climate that **dried out** our sinuses ______
3. **unusual** healing methods ______
4. a **frosted** piece of glass ______
5. **overjoyed** when the candidate lost ______

Writing: Words in Action

You are on a committee to improve lunches served in the school cafeteria. Write a brief essay suggesting three specific changes you think should be made and why such changes are necessary. Support each suggestion with personal observations, examples, and the reading (pages 24–25). Use three or more words from this Unit.

*Some of the words you have studied in this Unit appear in **boldface** type. Read the passage below, and then circle the letter of the correct answer for each word as it is used in context.*

The food guide pyramid was first introduced by the United States Department of Agriculture in 1992. Since then, it has been updated several times. In 2011, a redesigned version was named MyPlate. Despite these changes, the food pyramid retains the primary goal of informing us, the consumers, about the basic food groups and recommending how many servings of each group we should eat every day. In short, it is a tool we can all use to **lubricate** our creaky understanding of how to make healthier food choices.

The pyramid is divided into four levels and contains a total of six sections. At the bottom are the grains: bread, cereal, rice, and pasta. On the next level are the vegetables and fruits, while nearer the top are the dairy products and meat, poultry, and nuts. Finally, at the apex, are fats, oils, and sweets.

If we study the pyramid carefully, several food facts become clear. The five major food groups—grains, vegetables, fruits, dairy, and meat—work in **mutual** cooperation to keep us healthy. We would be wise to follow the recommendations of the food pyramid and not surrender to a fast-food **regime** where foods can have excess amounts of sugar, salt, and unhealthy fats. It is only a slight exaggeration to say that these three ingredients are bent on **homicide**. Should we regularly consume a diet of foods high in these three villains, we would be lucky to emerge with our health **unscathed**.

With the food pyramid, you can easily play the part of an **entrepreneur** in designing healthful and enjoyable school lunches. It's up to you! You can have a hand in promoting the recommendations outlined in the food pyramid.

---

1. What is the meaning of **lubricate** as it is used in paragraph 1?

a. break down **c.** bring closer
b. make easier **d.** make shiny

2. **Mutual** comes from the Latin word **mutuus**. **Mutuus** most likely means

a. silent **c.** proud
b. respected **d.** shared

3. The word **regime** means about the same as

a. rule **c.** menu
b. tyranny **d.** emphasis

4. What does the word **homicide** most likely mean as it is used in paragraph 3?

a. envy **c.** revenge
b. attack **d.** killing

5. Which word means the same as **unscathed** as it is used in paragraph 3?

a. injured **c.** intact
b. lengthy **d.** nimble

6. What is the meaning of **entrepreneur** as it is used in paragraph 4?

a. student **c.** businessperson
b. food professional **d.** novice

*Read the following passage, taking note of the **boldface** words and their contexts. These words are among those you will be studying in Unit 3. It may help you to complete the exercises in this Unit if you refer to the way the words are used below.*

Lunch at Delmonico's

<Diary Entry>

October 18, 1876

I've had little rest since arriving in New York on business. Harriet and I feel at home at the Fifth Avenue Hotel, which has proved a fine and **downright** respectable establishment. Today she set off early, in a quick and **animated** spirit, to meet with a certain ladies' group downtown. No doubt the whole **brood** spent the afternoon discussing women's suffrage. That topic has entirely absorbed my wife's attention of late, whenever she has not been **seething** with excitement about going to the theater. I've promised Harriet I will **indulge** myself by joining her along with her sister and Mr. Treadwell at the theater this evening.

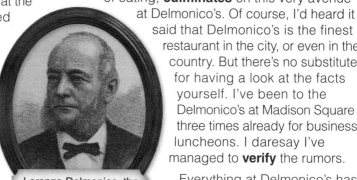

Lorenzo Delmonico, the restaurant's namesake

The food here in New York City is quite good. It seems the art of cooking, and with it the sport of eating, **culminates** on this very avenue at Delmonico's. Of course, I'd heard it said that Delmonico's is the finest restaurant in the city, or even in the country. But there's no substitute for having a look at the facts yourself. I've been to the Delmonico's at Madison Square three times already for business luncheons. I daresay I've managed to **verify** the rumors.

Everything at Delmonico's has the **luster** of elegance and good taste. The walls are lined with great mirrors. The furnishings are fine mahogany. Silver chandeliers hang from a painted ceiling.

View of Delmonico's restaurant on the corner of Fifth Avenue and 26th Street, New York City, c. 1888

Society people dining at Delmonico's in New York City, c. 1890

In the center of the main dining room there is a large fountain surrounded by flowers. This room enjoys a view of Fifth Avenue, and the well-placed diner can see a well-kept lawn and the trees and gardens of Madison Square. If he forgets to look up from his table, he'll be delighted almost as much by the craft of every **miscellaneous** detail, from the tablecloth to the silverware. I kept my eye open for an Astor or Vanderbilt to walk in, but I have yet to see one of the many wealthy and powerful men who frequent Delmonico's.

The menus are entirely in French. I confess at first I was somewhat **peevish** and put-off at being forced to choose between guessing what I should order and begging the help of some translator. The **upright** waiters of the establishment have been of some help in this regard, although my New York associates seem almost as well acquainted with the menu. A few **constituents** of the menu alarmed me—there was one dish consisting primarily of snails. But my companion on that occasion, Mr. Jameson, managed to **goad** me into trying it. After my initial shock, I found it a delicate and perfectly delicious dish.

I was also persuaded to try the delicious Lobster à la Wenberg. I'm told this is a new concoction of the chef's. I must say, however, that having sampled a great variety of dishes that were new and **unique** to me, I began last night to **hanker** for a good piece of beef. The Steak Delmonico I enjoyed for lunch this afternoon was as fine a cut as I've tasted anywhere out West. The chef cooks them to the customer's preference. I ordered mine rare and slightly **singed**.

In fact, I've just returned from that meal, which I took alone. It's left me in fine spirits (whoever said "the more the merrier" got it wrong). For the moment, I've forgotten about the work ahead of me tomorrow. I suppose an evening at the theater with Harriet and the Treadwells will do me some good after all.

Audio

For iWords and audio passages, go to **SadlierConnect.com**.

Definitions

Note the spelling, pronunciation, part(s) of speech, and definition(s) of each of the following words. Then write the appropriate form of the word in the blank space in the illustrative sentence(s) following.

1. brood (brüd)

(*n.*) a family of young animals, especially birds; any group having the same nature and origin; (*v.*) to think over in a worried, unhappy way

The mother bird fed her ____________________.

The pioneers did not ____________________ over the hardships they suffered on the long journey.

2. culminate (kəl′ mə nāt)

(*v.*) to reach a high point of development; to end, climax

The President's military advisors hoped the overseas action would not ____________________ in disaster.

3. drone (drōn)

(*n.*) a loafer, idler; a buzzing or humming sound; a remote-control device; a male bee; (*v.*) to make a buzzing sound; to speak in a dull tone of voice

The steady ____________________ of the engine put us all to sleep.

The speaker ____________________ on and on, ignoring the fact that much of the audience had left.

4. indulge (in dəlj′)

(*v.*) to give in to a wish or desire, give oneself up to

Sometimes the members of a losing team will ____________________ in self-pity.

5. literate (lit′ ə rət)

(*adj.*) able to read and write; showing an excellent educational background; having knowledge or training

Compared with others in the colonial settlement, she was a highly ____________________ young woman.

6. luster (ləs′ tər)

(*n.*) the quality of giving off light, brightness, glitter

The polished gold dome atop the state capitol shone with a starry ____________________.

7. oration (ô rā′ shən)

(*n.*) a public speech for a formal occasion

Cicero's ____________________ in the Roman Senate are still studied by speakers today.

8. peevish (pē′ vish)

(*adj.*) cross, complaining, irritable; contrary

Although the members of the tour group were usually in good humor, hunger made them ____________________.

9. singe (sinj) (*v.*) to burn slightly; (*n.*) a burn at the ends or edges

Getting too close to the flame of the campfire caused the camper to ____________________ his eyelashes.

A ____________________ from a cigar ash had destroyed the last word in the document.

10. upright (əp′ rīt) (*adj.*) vertical, straight; good, honest; (*adv.*) in a vertical position

The senator showed her ____________________ character by voting for bills she believed to be morally right.

The patient was finally standing ____________________.

Using Context

*For each item, determine whether the **boldface** word from pages 38–39 makes sense in the context of the sentence. Circle the item numbers next to the six sentences in which the words are used correctly.*

1. As the pilot prepared the plane for landing, the flight attendant requested that the passengers return their seats to an **upright** position.
2. I am not **literate** in coding or other computer science skills, but I plan to change that by taking courses during the summer.
3. Fairy tales often **culminate** with the words "once upon a time."
4. A **peevish** attitude is not appropriate for anyone whose job involves dealing with the public.
5. In her opening argument, the lawyer promised that the evidence would **indulge** the jury to find her client not guilty of the crime.
6. It can be very soothing to sit on a covered porch on a summer day and listen to the **luster** of a steady rain.
7. After a difficult year-long voyage, the ship was finally in sight of its **oration**, a group of small islands in the Caribbean Sea.
8. When the air conditioner began to **drone**, we feared that it was about to break down and we would have to replace it.
9. A mother alligator will defend her **brood** by fiercely hissing at any intruder.
10. The **singe** on the wooden spoon was caused when it was left too close to the flame on the stovetop.

Choosing the Right Word

*Select the **boldface** word that better completes each sentence. You might refer to the passage on pages 36–37 to see how most of these words are used in context. Note that the choices might be related forms of the Unit words.*

1. Anyone who strives to be (**peevish, literate**) in American literature should be familiar with the strange, mysterious tales of Edgar Allan Poe.

2. Instead of (**droning, brooding**) about the misfortunes that have befallen you, why don't you go out and do something to correct the situation?

3. It's all right for us to disagree, but let's argue about the facts only, without (**indulging, droning**) in name-calling.

4. Probably no (**oration, luster**) in American history is so well known and beloved as Lincoln's address on the battlefield of Gettysburg.

5. Each year the professional football season (**culminates, broods**) in the Super Bowl.

6. The school board candidate delivered a stirring, twenty-minute (**luster, oration**) on her plans for lowering the district's dropout rate.

7. It was really difficult to hear the speaker because of the steady (**oration, drone**) of airplanes landing, taxiing, and taking off.

8. I have my doubts about people who spend too much time telling the world how noble and (**upright, literate**) they are.

9. The last thing I heard before falling asleep was the (**brood, drone**) of their voices as they continued their endless discussion of politics.

10. You may make friends very easily, but if you continue to be so (**peevish, upright**), you aren't going to keep them for long.

11. The (**luster, oration**) of her reputation as a friend of humanity has grown brighter with the years.

12. "If you choose to play with fire," I warned them, "you run the risk of (**brooding, singeing**) your fingers."

Completing the Sentence

Choose the word from the word bank that best completes each of the following sentences. Write the correct word or form of the word in the space provided.

brood	drone	literate	oration	singe
culminate	indulge	luster	peevish	upright

1. Like the traffic guard at a school crossing, the mother hen directed her large ____________________ across the yard toward a torn sack of feed.

2. The sunlight shining on her hair gave it an almost metallic ____________________.

3. The mayor will deliver her annual Fourth of July ____________________ in City Square right after the parade.

4. We put supports around the tree that had been partially uprooted by the storm, and it was soon standing ____________________ again.

5. "You're just supposed to ____________________ the meat," I shouted at him in dismay, "not burn it to a crisp!"

6. I'm normally fairly even-tempered, but I can become ____________________ and irritable when I'm tired or frustrated.

7. The resentment of the American colonists against the harsh policies of the British government ____________________ in armed rebellion.

8. I don't know which is worse—parents who are too strict with their children or parents who ____________________ them too much.

9. Because of limited resources, only one half of the population of that underdeveloped nation is ____________________.

10. How pleasant it is for us city dwellers to smell the new-mown hay and listen to the ____________________ of bees in the clover patch!

End Set A

Definitions

Note the spelling, pronunciation, part(s) of speech, and definition(s) of each of the following words. Then write the appropriate form of the word in the blank space in the illustrative sentence(s) following.

1. animated (an′ ə māt id)
(*adj.*) full of life, lively, alive; (*part.*) moved to action
After the game the sportscaster found the winning team to be in an ____________ mood.

2. constituent (kən stich′ ə wənt)
(*n.*) an essential part; a voter who elects a representative
In our district, almost every ____________ is dedicated to participating in the voting process.

3. downright (daůn′ rīt)
(*adv.*) thoroughly; (*adj.*) absolute, complete; frank, blunt
Our neighbor, who chopped down our tree and destroyed our fence, is just ____________ mean.
The actor felt like a ____________ fool when he forgot his lines.

4. goad (gōd)
(*v.*) to drive or urge on; (*n.*) something used to drive or urge on
The sergeant had to ____________ the reluctant soldiers into action.
The cowhand used a ____________ to prod the sluggish cattle.

5. hanker (haŋ′ kər)
(*v.*) to long (for), to desire
Now after three weeks on the road, I really ____________ for home-cooked meals and my own bed.

6. loom (lüm)
(*v.*) to come into view; to appear in exaggerated form; (*n.*) a machine for weaving
The climbers were awestruck to see the peak ____________ up before them.
The antique ____________, once used to make cloth, was on display in the crafts museum.

7. miscellaneous (mis ə lā′ nē əs)
(*adj.*) mixed, of different kinds
A collection of ____________ items was gathering dust in the attic.

8. seethe (sēth)
(*v.*) to boil or foam; to be excited or disturbed
Mother would ____________ with rage each time she learned that a dog had been mistreated.

9. unique (yü nēk′) — (*adj.*) one of a kind; unequaled; unusual; found only in a given class, place, or situation

Most people would agree that finding an elephant in one's bathtub would constitute a ____________________ situation, even in one's dreams.

10. verify (ver′ ə fī) — (*v.*) to establish the truth or accuracy of, confirm

The reporter hurried to ____________________ the source of the controversial statement.

Using Context

*For each item, determine whether the **boldface** word from pages 42–43 makes sense in the context of the sentence. Circle the item numbers next to the six sentences in which the words are used correctly.*

1. I tried to **goad** the toddler to take her first steps by putting her favorite toy a few steps away, but she decided to crawl to it instead.
2. Although that rumor sounds fascinating, I suggest you **verify** its origin to make sure you're not simply spreading gossip.
3. I read over the **constituent**, hoping to find a clause that would allow me to get out of my responsibilities without penalty.
4. His **animated** voice suggested that he'd already had a long, hard day and could not handle any more stress.
5. I heard my stomach growl as the smell of dinner began to **seethe** throughout the house.
6. I proceeded to **hanker** my older brother into driving me to the mall until he was so annoyed that he gave in.
7. When I described her sense of fashion as **unique**, she did not realize that though her clothing is one of a kind, I did not find it particularly flattering.
8. I could not push back the doubt that began to **loom** in my mind over whether or not my supposed friend was actually trustworthy.
9. The **miscellaneous** items I found in my purse when I went to clean it out included old receipts, business cards, and some old lip balm.
10. When my science partner played a video game as I did all the work, I accused him of being **downright** lazy.

Set B

Choosing the Right Word

*Select the **boldface** word that better completes each sentence. You might refer to the passage on pages 36–37 to see how most of these words are used in context. Note that the choices might be related forms of the Unit words.*

1. Even those who do not like New York must admit that it is a truly (**unique, animated**) city, quite unlike any other in the world.
2. Though the colonies had long (**seethed, hankered**) with resentment at the British, the cauldron of their discontent did not boil over into rebellion until 1776.
3. All the students in Sandra's advanced weaving class are making small rugs on their portable (**looms, goads**).
4. Modern scientists often try to (**loom, verify**) their ideas and theories by conducting extensive experiments in their laboratories.
5. On a cold night, what I (**goad, hanker**) for most is a hot bowl of chicken soup.
6. The man was not just "a little careless" in handling the club's funds; he was (**downright, animatedly**) dishonest!
7. The American people must take action right now to deal with the problem of pollution that (**looms, seethes**) so large on our horizon.
8. An important (**constituent, loom**) of what is commonly called luck is the willingness to take chances when an opportunity appears.
9. Neither threats nor force will (**hanker, goad**) me into doing something that in my heart I know is wrong.
10. In his many years in Congress, he has been (**animated, miscellaneous**) mainly by a strong desire to help the underdogs in our society.
11. Glenn has such a store of (**miscellaneous, downright**) information in his head that we have nicknamed him "The Encyclopedia"!
12. By Friday afternoon, all of us were (**verifying, hankering**) for a relaxing, enjoyable weekend.

Completing the Sentence

Choose the word from the word bank that best completes each of the following sentences. Write the correct word or form of the word in the space provided.

animated	**downright**	**hanker**	**miscellaneous**	**unique**
constituent	**goad**	**loom**	**seethe**	**verify**

1. Larry has the ____________________ distinction of being the only student in our school ever to win varsity letters in four sports.

2. Like some storm-tossed sea, her inventive brain ____________________ with all kinds of new and imaginative answers to old problems and questions.

3. When storm clouds ____________________ on the horizon, we hurried to find shelter.

4. In every election, the candidates try to persuade their ____________________ that they know how to solve the problems and issues that most concern them.

5. Indian elephant keepers usually use a short wooden ____________________ to control and direct the movements of their huge charges.

6. When I saw how handsome my father looked in his brand-new jacket, I ____________________ for one exactly like it.

7. I believe in being careful, but Dan is ____________________ miserly when it comes to spending money.

8. The dull conversation became much more ____________________ when it turned to a subject in which we were all interested.

9. The man was the prime suspect in the crime until two eyewitnesses came forward to ____________________ his alibi.

10. Those books that do not fit logically under any of the subjects indicated will be placed in a group labeled "____________________."

End Set B

Synonyms

*Choose the word or form of the word from this Unit that is the same or most nearly the same in meaning as the **boldface** word or expression in the phrase. Write that word on the line. Use a dictionary if necessary.*

1. gave a long **sermon** ____________
2. offered a **singular** opportunity ____________
3. lost some of its **brilliance** with each performance ____________
4. told not to **agonize** over the details ____________
5. the key **ingredient** in the process ____________
6. the **crabby**, teething baby ____________
7. had to **substantiate** his claims ____________
8. tree branches **scorched** by the fire ____________
9. propped in a **vertical** position ____________
10. **simmering** with anger ____________
11. despite the danger that **appears** ahead ____________
12. **coddle** their grandchildren ____________
13. attempted to **incite** others into action ____________
14. **crave** Paris in the springtime ____________
15. an **utter** disaster ____________

Antonyms

*Choose the word or form of the word from this Unit that is most nearly opposite in meaning to the **boldface** word or expression in the phrase. Write that word on the line. Use a dictionary if necessary.*

1. had a deserved reputation as a **workaholic** ____________
2. a campaign that will **commence** in a week ____________
3. was completely **unschooled** in physics and calculus ____________
4. a story told in a **flat** tone ____________
5. a group of **identical** shapes ____________

Writing: Words in Action

Published diaries offer firsthand accounts of certain historical events and eras. In your opinion, is it helpful to learn about the past from a specific person's personal experiences? In a brief essay, explain your reasoning. Use examples from your reading (pages 36–37) and three or more words from this Unit.

Vocabulary in Context

*Some of the words you have studied in this Unit appear in **boldface** type. Read the passage below, and then circle the letter of the correct answer for each word as it is used in context.*

Hunger relief organizations exist on local, national, and international levels. City Harvest, which operates in New York City, is an example of the first, while the National Restaurant Association exemplifies the second. Global FoodBanking Network, an example of the third, operates in 32 countries. Taken together, these organizations comprise a **unique** effort to relieve hunger in today's world.

According to the National Restaurant Association, nearly 40 percent of all food production in the United States is wasted. What statistic could **loom** larger in a call for social reform? We don't need to have a persuasive **oration** or newspaper editorial urging change; we just need to use our common sense.

A **literate**, balanced inquiry shows that there are two major streams of waste in restaurants. Pre-consumer waste commonly involves overproduction. Restaurant owners and managers overbuy to hedge against the risk of running out of a particular item. Post-consumer waste is food that is left on customers' plates after the meal.

Restaurant managers have no need to **drone** on about the difficulty of tracking food waste, says one expert. It should take less than 15 minutes a week for a chef to **verify** food waste data with the kitchen team. One executive of the National Restaurant Association emphasizes the role of incentives. According to this observer, owners, chefs, and their teams will respond effectively if the issue of waste is presented to them in moral terms. Anyone who reduces waste should receive professional recognition and positive reinforcement.

---

1. **Unique** comes from the Latin word **unicus**. **Unicus** most likely means

a. broad **c.** lasting
b. only **d.** fine

2. What is the meaning of **loom** as it is used in paragraph 2?

a. dominate **c.** exclaim
b. signify **d.** emerge

3. What is the meaning of **oration** as it is used in paragraph 2?

a. address **c.** analysis
b. conflict **d.** breakthrough

4. The word **literate** means about the same as

a. prudent **c.** decisive
b. educated **d.** sustained

5. Which word means the same as **drone** as it is used in paragraph 4?

a. stumble clumsily **c.** speak dully
b. retreat quickly **d.** resound loudly

6. What does the word **verify** most likely mean as it is used in paragraph 4?

a. interrogate **c.** validate
b. categorize **d.** correlate

Vocabulary for Comprehension

Part 1

*Read "A Llama's Odd Job," which contains words in **boldface** that appear in Units 1–3. Then answer the questions.*

The Llama's Odd Job

For thousands of years, the llama has been a working animal. In fact, in the **barren**, rugged highlands of Peru, this **unique** animal has for centuries proved to be a reliable beast of burden, carrying heavy packs to lowland markets.

In just one day, a llama can travel 20 miles while carrying 50–75 pounds on its back. Sometimes hundreds of llamas travel together like this. These vegetarians eat many different kinds of plants. Llamas are related to camels and do not need much water to survive, so they are well suited to their work in Peru's mountains.

About one hundred years ago, the llama was brought to the United States. In this country, the llama has added to its **résumé** by gaining some unusual work experience, so strange in fact that here its "odd job" has all but replaced its **customary** use as a pack animal.

Because of its tendency to work hard, eat cheaply, go many miles without water, and get along well with people and other animals, the llama has proved to be a match for many other working animals. Yet it is not just in **trivial** matters, such as carrying golf bags (although llamas do serve as caddies) or in maintaining hiking trails (they do work for the National Park Service), that llamas have distinguished themselves in this country. In fact, in the United States, the llama's true calling seems to be in "predator protection," acting as a kind of fantastic "sheepdog."

Interestingly, llamas make good "guard dogs" for the following reasons: They are quick studies, learning in a few days what might take a dog a year to master. Also, llamas and sheep get along famously. Most important, llamas have a natural distaste for coyotes, the sheep's main predator, and they don't get frazzled in the face of danger. When brazen predators approach the herd, llamas aggressively chase away the intruders. They also possess a **vicious** kick that they use should a predator come too close.

So serious is this problem that in the United States predators are said to have killed millions of dollars worth of sheep in the past few years. Although efforts have been under way to destroy the coyotes, the focus now is on protecting the sheep. It would seem that the best way to do that is to "hire" a llama. In fact, when interviewed in an Iowa study, half the llama-owning sheep farmers reported sheep losses down to zero since getting a llama, which just goes to show that there's nothing like having a good guard dog, especially when it's a llama.

1. Which sentence **best** states the author's purpose in "A Llama's Odd Job"?
   A) The author explains the difference between llamas and sheepdogs.
   B) The author informs the reader about a nontraditional use of llamas.
   C) The author persuades the reader of the benefits of raising llamas.
   D) The author describes the physical characteristics of a llama.

2. What does **barren** (line 3) most likely mean?
   A) lush
   B) unproductive
   C) boring
   D) fertile

3. What does the word **unique** in line 4 suggest about the llama?
   A) It is distinctive.
   B) It is friendly.
   C) It is aggressive.
   D) It is commonplace.

4. **Part A**
   As it is used in this passage, what does the word **customary** (line 20) mean?
   A) legal
   B) traditional
   C) untraditional
   D) reliable

   Part B
   Which evidence from "A Llama's Odd Job" supports the answer to Part A?
   A) "reliable beast of burden, carrying heavy packs" (lines 5–6)
   B) "gaining some unusual work experience" (line 18)
   C) "true calling seems to be in 'predator protection'" (lines 33–34)
   D) "a natural distaste for coyotes, the sheep's main predator" (lines 41–42)

5. What does the word **résumé** most likely mean as it is used in line 17?
   A) story
   B) experience
   C) work history
   D) qualifications

6. According to the article, what are **trivial** matters?
   A) insignificant matters
   B) entertaining matters
   C) important matters
   D) exceptional matters

7. From paragraphs 1 and 2 (lines 1–14), what can you infer is a llama's usual work?
   A) maintaining hiking trails
   B) carrying golf bags
   C) protecting sheep
   D) carrying heavy burdens

8. Which sentence describes the overall structure of lines 36–48?
   A) The text provides reasons llamas do a job well.
   B) The text compares llamas and sheep.
   C) The text contrasts llamas and coyotes.
   D) The text describes llamas' predators.

9. According to the article, what is a **vicious** kick?
   A) a swift kick
   B) a painful kick
   C) a warning kick
   D) a natural kick

10. Why does the author **most likely** refer to an Iowa study in lines 56–60?
    A) to explain how many farmers use llamas to protect sheep
    B) to provide a theory about why llamas are good workers
    C) to describe how llamas and sheep behave together
    D) to give a statistic that supports other information

Vocabulary for Comprehension Part 2

*Read this passage, which contains words in **boldface** that appear in Units 1–3. Then choose the best answer to each question based on what is stated or implied in the passage. You may refer to the passage as often as necessary.*

Questions 1–10 are based on the following passage.

In December 1781, the Americans and French defeated the British at the Battle of Yorktown. This victory forced the British to surrender, ending the seemingly **interminable** American Revolution. In April 1782, the Continental Congress selected five of its **constituents** to negotiate a treaty in Paris. These members were John Adams, Benjamin Franklin, John Jay, Thomas Jefferson, and Henry Laurens. Henry Laurens, however, was captured by a British warship and held in the Tower of London until the end of the war. Thomas Jefferson did not leave the United States in time for the negotiations. In order not to **hinder** the process, Laurens and Jefferson did not participate in negotiations for the Treaty of Paris.

On September 3, 1783, John Adams, Benjamin Franklin, and John Jay signed the Treaty of Paris with Great Britain. The Treaty of Paris was written to formally **culminate** the American Revolution. The Treaty of Paris had 10 articles that responded to demands that the United States had made of Britain. Article 1 of the Treaty of Paris recognized the independence of the United States from the British **regime**. Article 1 stated: "His Britannic Majesty acknowledges the said United States ... to be free sovereign and independent states." This article also asserted that the king "relinquishes all claims to the government, propriety, and territorial rights of the same and every part thereof."

Article 2 of the Treaty of Paris ceded British control over much of the land **adjacent** to the 13 colonies. This territory included all land between the Allegheny Mountains in the east and the Mississippi River in the west. This expanded U.S. territory excluded Canada. By defining these boundaries, the Treaty of Paris guaranteed American westward expansion. Article 2 of the Treaty of Paris also doubled the size of the young nation.

Another provision of the Treaty of Paris was to ensure that American fishermen had access to fisheries in Canadian waters. Article 3 of the Treaty of Paris stated: "It is agreed that the people of the United States shall continue to enjoy unmolested the right to take fish of every kind on the Grand Bank and on all the other banks of Newfoundland, also in the Gulf of Saint Lawrence and at all other places in the sea, where the inhabitants of both countries used at any time heretofore to fish."

Seven additional articles comprised the Treaty of Paris. These articles addressed **miscellaneous** subjects ranging from navigating the Mississippi River to **recompensing** debts. The Treaty of Paris was an **indispensable** document in American history because it established the foundation of the United States.

1. According to the passage, why was the Battle of Yorktown important?
   A) The Battle of Yorktown caused Henry Laurens's capture.
   B) The Battle of Yorktown hindered treaty negotiations.
   C) The Battle of Yorktown was the most interminable fight.
   D) The Battle of Yorktown ended the American Revolution.

2. As it is used in line 5, the word "interminable" means
   A) complicated.
   B) endless.
   C) strategic.
   D) impossible.

3. What is the main idea of paragraph 2 (lines 19–36)?
   A) Article 1 was the most significant article in the Treaty of Paris.
   B) John Adams, Benjamin Franklin, and John Jay signed the Treaty of Paris.
   C) The Treaty of Paris ended the American Revolution and recognized America's independence.
   D) Each article in the Treaty of Paris responded to demands that the United States made of Great Britain.

4. As it is used in line 23, the word "culminate" means
   A) to end.
   B) to intensify.
   C) to lengthen.
   D) to force.

5. According to the passage, what land did Article 2 of the Treaty of Paris grant to the United States?
   A) The original 13 colonies to the eastern border of the Allegheny Mountains
   B) The Mississippi River to the west and Canada to the north
   C) All land between the Allegheny Mountains in the east and the Mississippi River in the west
   D) The Allegheny Mountains to the Mississippi River, including Canada

6. Why does the author include lines 52-60?
   A) The quotation provides direct evidence for the main idea of the paragraph.
   B) The quotation reveals the specific fish that American fishermen can access.
   C) The quotation names specific fisheries in the Gulf of St. Lawrence.
   D) The quotation compares the Grand Bank with the banks of Newfoundland.

7. As it is used in line 39, the word "adjacent" means
   A) next to.
   B) aligned with.
   C) equal to.
   D) owned by.

8. According to the author of this passage, the Treaty of Paris
   A) caused the British to surrender at Yorktown.
   B) would have been expedited if Laurens and Jefferson had attended.
   C) granted land to Canada and the United States.
   D) was one of the most important documents in American history.

9. As it is used in line 66, the word "indispensable" means
   A) formally written.
   B) absolutely necessary.
   C) selectively enforced.
   D) fairly negotiated.

10. What is the central idea of this passage?
    A) The Battle of Yorktown was the final battle of the American Revolution.
    B) Articles 1, 2, and 3 in the Treaty of Paris were more important than other articles.
    C) The Treaty of Paris granted land, independence, and rights to the new United States.
    D) The Treaty of Paris doubled the size of the United States and ensured westward expansion.

*From the word bank below, choose the word that has the same or nearly the same meaning as the **boldface** word in each sentence and write it on the line. You will not use all of the words.*

barren	**downright**	**interrogate**	**seethe**
cater	**entrepreneur**	**luster**	**sullen**
culminate	**foretaste**	**mutual**	**verify**
dissuade	**insinuate**	**renovate**	**vicious**

1. My brother could have possibly saved so much money from his allowance alone, so I began to **question** him on where it came from. ________________
2. She was not only a great chef, but also a savvy **businessperson** whose new restaurant was booked months in advance. ________________
3. The director's decision to **conclude** the movie with a cliffhanger suggests that there is a sequel already in production. ________________
4. When my friend asked what was bothering me, I realized I was not hiding my **grumpy** mood as well as I thought. ________________
5. While I understand why the character in the novel seeks revenge on those who wronged him, I do not think his enemies' actions warrant such **malicious** payback. ________________
6. The short comedy sketch released by the writers of the new series offers an exciting **preview** of what the show will be like. ________________
7. I scrubbed the kitchen until every surface sparkled with a **sheen**. ________________
8. Although he maintains he was simply "stretching the truth," I would describe him as nothing but an **out-and-out** liar. ________________
9. Since my sister claimed she knocked over the vase on her way to come help me in the kitchen, I asked if she was trying to **imply** that I was responsible for her mistake. ________________
10. There is nothing so exciting as meeting a new friend and quickly feeling a **reciprocal** affinity for one another. ________________
11. Even when I tried to go to sleep, my mind continued to **churn** with thoughts of the day's events. ________________
12. Since no one was home to provide a signature that would **prove** they received the package, it was sent back to the manufacturer. ________________

Two-Word Completions

Select the pair of words that best completes the meaning of each of the following sentences.

1. Winds fanned the flames, and the fire on the upper floors of the factory quickly spread to ____________ buildings. Though firefighters worked valiantly to ____________ its progress, the blaze soon engulfed the entire block.

a. miscellaneous ... animate
b. adjacent ... hinder
c. available ... goad
d. upright ... germinate

2. When the new ____________ took office, its first order of business was to pacify the country by arranging a ____________ with the rebel forces that had been waging all-out war against the previous administration.

a. regime ... truce
b. firebrand ... résumé
c. dynasty ... plague
d. drone ... homicide

3. When I was very young, I truly ____________ a life of excitement, adventure, and danger. But now that I'm a good deal older, I'm perfectly content with my rather ____________ existence.

a. alighted on ... trivial
b. indulged in ... peevish
c. hankered for ... humdrum
d. brooded about ... interminable

4. Though crabmeat is the ____________ ingredient in the classic recipe for a New Orleans fish stew, it isn't always in season. Professional chefs often replace it with whatever shellfish is ____________ at the time, without any noticeable damage to the dish.

a. unique ... indispensable
b. customary ... available
c. upright ... transparent
d. humdrum ... adjacent

5. Running our country is full of all kinds of hidden ____________ and traps for the unwary. For that reason, no president, no matter how alert or cautious, ever leaves office entirely ____________ by the experience.

a. firebrands ... poised
b. regimes ... lubricated
c. hazards ... unscathed
d. orations ... animated

6. At one point in last night's hockey game, home-team fans became so angry with the referee that they began to ____________ him with refuse. Programs, paper cups, and even a dead fish ____________ through the air and landed at his feet.

a. indulge ... loomed
b. singe ... trickled
c. disrupt ... droned
d. pelt ... hurtled

7. The speaker showed complete ____________ to the record heat and heavy downpour. He was ____________, however, when hecklers interrupted him for the fourth time.

a. indifference ... indignant
b. recompense ... indispensable
c. oration ... literate
d. constituent ... poised

WORD STUDY

In the passage "The Times of Zheng He" (see pages 12–13), the writer describes political unrest in fourteenth-century China by using the expression "a change was in the wind."

"A change in the wind" is an idiom that means a transformation of some kind will take place soon. An **idiom** is a figure of speech or an informal expression that is not meant literally. You learn idioms by hearing them used in daily conversation. Idioms can be fun to use in conversations, but because they are informal, use them sparingly in writing.

Choosing the Right Idiom

Read each sentence. Use context clues to figure out the meaning of each idiom in ***boldface*** *print. Then write the letter of the definition for the idiom in the sentence.*

1. Whatever you do, don't **upset the applecart** by telling Elena that you're quitting. ______
2. The mayor signed a bill pledging to have all city buildings **go green** within the next two years. ______
3. After you graduate, what do you plan to do to **bring home the bacon**? ______
4. Of all the dogs in the rescue shelter, only one, a black Scottish terrier, **caught my eye**. ______
5. You know that Katie will **raise a stink** if she thinks she's been treated unfairly. ______
6. Marianela has been patient, but the next time you skip practice, she's going to **blow the whistle** on you. ______
7. After an hour of his scrubbing and polishing, the bathroom is **as clean as a whistle**. ______
8. I forgot that the party was a surprise, so I **let the cat out of the bag** when I asked Austin if he was going to attend it. ______
9. Marcus, who often speaks up without thinking, definitely needs to learn to **button his lip**. ______
10. Because of obesity's bad health effects, I've vowed to quit **cold turkey** on chocolate and other sweets. ______

a. stop talking
b. complain in a forceful way; make something into a big issue
c. attracted my attention
d. take steps to reduce pollution and save energy
e. spoil someone's plans; cause trouble
f. earn money; make a living
g. immediately and completely stop a bad habit
h. report misconduct or bad behavior
i. spotless
j. revealed something that's supposed to be secret

Classical Roots

pend, pens—to hang, weigh; to pay; to set aside

The Latin root *pens* appears in **indispensable** (page 30). That word's original meaning was "not able to be set aside or done away with," but now the word has come to mean "essential or necessary." Some other words based on the same root are listed below.

dependent	**dispense**	**expenditure**	**perpendicular**
dispensary	**expendable**	**pension**	**suspense**

From the list of words above, choose the one that corresponds to each of the brief definitions below. Write the word in the blank space in the illustrative sentence below the definition. Use a dictionary if necessary.

1. relying on another for help or support; determined or conditioned by something else; a person who is supported by another
A lion cub is ____________________ on its mother for nourishment.

2. to give out, distribute
It is a judge's duty to ____________________ justice with an even hand.

3. a fixed amount paid to retired employees or their families
At age 65, he will receive a small ____________________ from his company.

4. the amount of money spent; spending, using up (*"paying out"*)
Worrying is a needless ____________________ of energy.

5. the state of being uncertain or undecided; anxiety, nervous uncertainty
The audience was kept in ____________________ until the winner of the singing contest was announced.

6. a place where medicines are made or given out (*"place from which things are weighed out"*)
The nurse obtained the medicine she needed in the hospital ____________________.

7. replaceable, nonessential
It is difficult for some employees to realize that they are ____________________ and can be let go at any time.

8. at right angles; exactly upright, vertical
The wall is ____________________ to the floor.

UNIT 4

*Read the following passage, taking note of the **boldface** words and their contexts. These words are among those you will be studying in Unit 4. It may help you to complete the exercises in this Unit if you refer to the way the words are used below.*

Coyotes in Legend and Myth

<Informational Essay>

In some of the most **spirited** Native American myths and legends, the main character is a trickster figure named Coyote. In these tales, Coyote is nearly always **controversial**, inspiring both admiration and disapproval. Sometimes he is wily and ingenious, while at other times he plays the **buffoon**. At first glance, such paradoxes may seem **bewildering**.

But Coyote's great achievement as a mythical figure is to break the **orthodox** mold. In the end, he cannot be easily classified. It is usually **fruitless** to predict how Coyote will behave in any given situation. He is a **virtual** bundle of contradictions. He is simultaneously a clown, a rebel, and a **wayward** troublemaker.

In myths and legends, the character Coyote displays some clear resemblances to the behavior of the animal known as *Canis latrans.* Like coyotes in real life, the story character is nearly always hungry. One of his primary concerns is to **procure** food to fill his belly. To this end, he **scurries** around, often in disguise and more than willing to cheat others.

One amusing tale about Coyote and cheating involves the challenge of a trader. This man dares Coyote to beat him in a deal. Far

from being **disheartened**, Coyote accepts the challenge. He tells the man, though, that he needs to return home to collect his "cheating medicine." Coyote will need to borrow the trader's horse. Also, to make the horse comfortable, he will need to borrow the trader's clothes. Eagerly, the trader gives in to these requests. As Coyote rides off into the distance, the trader, who had hoped to **inflict** a defeat on Coyote, is left **mortified** and **wincing** with shame.

In another tale, an opponent turns the tables on Coyote, bearing out the truth of the old adage "set a thief to catch a thief." As often in trickster tales, Coyote has forged an **alliance** with his friend Iktome, or Spider. The two friends admire a beautiful rock named Iya. Coyote places his own blanket on the rock as a gift. When the weather turns colder, however, Coyote reclaims the blanket, despite Iktome's warnings. After Coyote refuses to return the blanket, Iya turns **hostile**. Rolling through the woods, he pursues the two friends. Finally, Iktome dashes down a hole to escape, abandoning Coyote. Iya then rolls over Coyote, flattening him out like a rug. The trickster has been beaten. At least, so it appears.

Coyote is never permanently defeated, however. In Native American legends and myths, he always has the power to return to life. In fact, many of these stories present Coyote as the creator of the world. In these tales, he fashions the universe from the **void** and makes people out of mud. Coyote is also featured as a culture hero who steals fire and gives it to human beings. This dimension of Coyote parallels the most famous deed of the Greek mythological hero Prometheus, who was punished by the gods for his theft of fire.

In fact, Coyote as a trickster resembles many of the best-known figures of world mythology, such as Loki in northern Europe, the fox Reynard in medieval France, the Japanese kitsune or seven-tailed fox, and the trickster/creator figure of Raven, who is also a hero in many Native American tales.

Audio

For iWords and audio passages, go to **SadlierConnect.com.**

SadlierConnect.com: iWords Audio Program

Definitions

Note the spelling, pronunciation, part(s) of speech, and definition(s) of each of the following words. Then write the appropriate form of the word in the blank space in the illustrative sentence(s) following.

1. alliance (ə lī′ əns)
(*n.*) a joining together for some common purpose
The two nations formed an ____________________ to defend each other in case of attack.

2. bewilder (bi wil′ dər)
(*v.*) to puzzle completely, confuse
The captain continues to ____________________ his troops by giving contradictory orders.

3. fruitless (früt′ ləs)
(*adj.*) not producing the desired results, unsuccessful
When their efforts to fight the infection with penicillin proved ____________________, the doctors tried a new antibiotic.

4. inflammable (in flam′ ə bəl)
(*adj.*) easily set on fire; easily angered or aroused
Always be cautious when using ____________________ cleaning solvents.

5. mortify (môrt′ ə fī)
(*v.*) to hurt someone's feelings deeply; to cause embarrassment or humiliation; to subdue or discipline by self-denial or suffering
The teacher was ____________________ by the students' childish behavior on the field trip.

6. orthodox (ôr′ thə däks)
(*adj.*) in agreement with established or generally accepted beliefs or ways of doing things
Our principal, who believes in proven teaching methods, takes an ____________________ approach to education.

7. scurry (skər′ ē)
(*v.*) to run quickly, scamper, hurry
The reappearance of the teacher caused the students in the class to ____________________ back to their seats.

8. sodden (säd′ ən)
(*adj.*) soaked with liquid or moisture; expressionless, dull; spiritless, listless
All at once, and with much loud honking, the flock of geese rose from the ____________________ marshlands.

9. wayward (wā′ wərd) — (*adj.*) disobedient, willful; unpredictable, capricious

Tracking the ____________ path of a comet is no easy matter.

10. wince (wins) — (*v.*) to draw back suddenly, as though in pain or fear; (*n.*) the act of drawing back in this way

The animal's bite made the child ____________ in pain.

The patient's ____________ told the doctor to press more gently.

Using Context

*For each item, determine whether the **boldface** word from pages 58–59 makes sense in the context of the sentence. Circle the item numbers next to the six sentences in which the words are used correctly.*

1. The warning label indicated that the liquid inside the container was **inflammable** and should be kept away from heat.
2. A well-trained sheepherding dog knows how to move toward a **wayward** sheep in order to direct it to return to the rest of the flock.
3. If you are not careful about removing weeds when they first appear, they can completely **bewilder** your flower or vegetable garden.
4. It would **mortify** me to find out that I had made a bad impression on the job interviewer by bragging about my accomplishments.
5. That art student with the impressive range can paint both in an **orthodox** and an experimental style.
6. The toddler made a **fruitless** search for her doll and quickly found it under the bed.
7. Have you ever seen a little seabird called a sandpiper **scurry** back and forth on the wet sand as the waves come in and go out?
8. A heavy downpour is needed to revive this dry and **sodden** lawn.
9. I tried not to **wince** as the nurse stuck a needle in my arm in order to draw blood during my yearly physical examination.
10. Not only must you simply state your opinion in a persuasive piece of writing, you must also provide **alliance** for it.

Choosing the Right Word

*Select the **boldface** word that better completes each sentence. You might refer to the passage on pages 56–57 to see how most of these words are used in context. Note that the choices might be related forms of the Unit words.*

1. Being scolded for my shortcomings in front of the entire basketball squad was a (**mortifying, wayward**) experience for me.

2. Though her views about the role of women in society are far from (**fruitless, orthodox**), even conservatives and traditionalists listen to them.

3. On the hottest night of the summer, the sheets on my bed became so (**sodden, orthodox**) with perspiration that I had to change them.

4. Walking through the meadow at night, we could hear mice and other small animals (**scurrying, wincing**) in the grass.

5. We are going to form a broad (**wince, alliance**) among all the groups that are working to improve life in our community.

6. “Whenever you find (**wayward, orthodox**) children,” the speaker said, “you also find ineffective parents.”

7. I still (**scurry, wince**) when I think of the two errors that cost us the championship.

8. All our efforts to control pollution will be (**fruitless, inflammable**) unless we work out a careful, detailed plan in advance.

9. That joke was so unfunny, even the comedian herself gave a(n) (**alliance, wince**).

10. Our supervisor acts calm most of the time, but we have learned that he has a very (**orthodox, inflammable**) temper.

11. In general, they tend to write with an (**orthodoxy, alliance**) that reflects the principles of their ideology.

12. I could see from the (**winced, bewildered**) expression on the child’s face that he was lost.

Completing the Sentence

Choose the word from the word bank that best completes each of the following sentences. Write the correct word or form of the word in the space provided.

alliance	**fruitless**	**mortify**	**scurry**	**wayward**
bewilder	**inflammable**	**orthodox**	**sodden**	**wince**

1. Their behavior is so ____________________ and unpredictable that I never know what they are going to do next.

2. In 1949, the United States formed a(n) ____________________ with eleven other nations, calling it the North Atlantic Treaty Organization.

3. When the naughty children heard their mother's footsteps approaching, they quickly ____________________ back to bed.

4. I was thoroughly ____________________ when I suddenly stumbled and spilled punch all over the host's tuxedo.

5. After four days of steady rainfall, the ____________________ ground gurgled as we trudged wearily over it.

6. The directions he gave us for driving to the beach were so complicated that I was completely ____________________ by them.

7. Even though you like to do things in your own way, I suggest that you first learn the ____________________ method of batting.

8. Would it be a bad pun if I were to say that our attempts to set up an apple orchard have proved to be ____________________?

9. Even though I'm an adult, I still ____________________ in discomfort at the thought of a trip to the dentist.

10. Because the gas did not burn when we brought a flame to it, the experiment showed that carbon dioxide is not ____________________.

End Set A

Definitions

Note the spelling, pronunciation, part(s) of speech, and definition(s) of each of the following words. Then write the appropriate form of the word in the blank space in the illustrative sentence(s) following.

1. buffoon (bə fün′)
(*n.*) a clown; a coarse, stupid person
Some students think that they need to play the ____________ in order to entertain their classmates and charm their teachers.

2. controversial (kän trə vər′ shəl)
(*adj.*) arousing argument, dispute, or disagreement
The school board waited until all members were present before issuing the ____________ proposal to ban after-school programs.

3. dishearten (dis härt′ ən)
(*v.*) to discourage
Do not let your low score on the math test ____________ you.

4. hostile (häs′ təl)
(*adj.*) unfriendly; unfavorable; warlike, aggressive
Relations between the two nations have been ____________ for decades.

5. inflict (in flikt′)
(*v.*) to give or cause something unpleasant, impose
Despite all the jokes, doctors do not like to ____________ pain on their patients.

6. malignant (mə lig′ nənt)
(*adj.*) deadly, extremely harmful, evil; spiteful, malicious
Much to the patient's relief, the x-ray revealed no ____________ growth.

7. procure (prə kyür′)
(*v.*) to obtain through special effort; to bring about
The hospital held a raffle to ____________ the necessary funds for the new children's wing.

8. spirited (spir′ ə tid)
(*adj.*) full of life and vigor; courageous
The royal soldiers put up a ____________ defense against the invading army.

9. virtual (vər′ chü əl)
(*adj.*) having a certain force or effect in fact but not in name; so close as to be equivalent to the real thing

To those who worked in the office, the bossy new manager was a ________________ dictator.

10. void (void)
(*adj.*) completely empty; having no legal force or effect; (*n.*) empty or unfilled space; (*v.*) to cancel or nullify

I thought that poem was completely ________________ of sense.

Grandmother's death left a great ________________ in my grandfather's life.

Do you know how to ________________ a check?

Using Context

For each item, determine whether the ***boldface*** *word from pages 62–63 makes sense in the context of the sentence. Circle the item numbers next to the six sentences in which the words are used correctly.*

1. The contract was deemed **void** when we learned it had been signed by a minor.
2. When the conversation began to **procure** into nothing but complaints about school and work, I chose to excuse myself from the conversation.
3. I offered some **hostile** words of comfort to a friend in need.
4. I apologize for my careless words and promise that I did not intend to **inflict** pain on you.
5. When I brought up the issue of what the theme should be for the homecoming dance at the student council meeting, I didn't expect it to be such a **controversial** topic.
6. The images of shelter animals who need permanent homes always **dishearten** me so much that I have adopted six pets already.
7. We felt relief when we learned that the growth on my arm was not **malignant**.
8. Although the two disagree on many points, they are always able to have **spirited** debates that stimulate others' interest rather than fighting with each other.
9. My little sister acts like a **buffoon** when she wants a favor from me, suddenly being sweet and complimenting me nonstop.
10. Most high school seniors feel that they are **virtual** graduates already and tend to slack off toward the end of the year.

Set B

Choosing the Right Word

*Select the **boldface** word that better completes each sentence. You might refer to the passage on pages 56–57 to see how most of these words are used in context. Note that the choices might be related forms of the Unit words.*

1. When his army seemed (**virtually, controversially**) defeated by the British, George Washington crossed the Delaware and won a victory.

2. Instead of being (**spirited, hostile**), why don't you try to show some friendliness to those newcomers?

3. The scrappy coach's (**malignant, spirited**) pep talk lifted the team out of its "losing-season blues."

4. (**Virtual, Controversial**) political figures are likely to have as many outspoken critics as enthusiastic supporters.

5. (**Malignant, Virtual**) gossip has unjustly damaged their reputation.

6. A cold spell in December (**inflicted, procured**) heavy losses on the Florida citrus crop.

7. In high school, students should (**procure, void**) training in basic skills that they will need in order to get good jobs as adults.

8. For this job, we hope to hire people who have a (**spirited, disheartened**) and upbeat attitude, not ones who are drab and dull.

9. I can understand that you want to be witty and amusing, but try not to make people think you're a mere (**void, buffoon**).

10. "It's hard not to be a little (**procured, disheartened**) when your favorite team is in the cellar two weeks before the playoffs," I replied.

11. From the deck of the starship, they gazed in awe at the empty black (**buffoon, void**) of outer space.

12. Because I no longer go to high school, my student bus pass has been (**voided, disheartened**).

Completing the Sentence

Choose the word from the word bank that best completes each of the following sentences. Write the correct word or form of the word in the space provided.

buffoon	dishearten	inflict	procure	virtual
controversial	hostile	malignant	spirited	void

1. Though the gallant defenders of the fort were hopelessly outnumbered, they put up a truly ____________________ fight.
2. Before we set out on the camping trip, I was given sole responsibility for ____________________ all the equipment and supplies.
3. The frozen wastes of the Arctic may seem ____________________ to human life, but in fact thousands of people are able to survive there.
4. When the Supreme Court finds a law unconstitutional, that law is said to be null and ____________________.
5. The often dreary courts of medieval kings were enlivened by the pranks and antics of jesters and ____________________.
6. Some parts of the President's proposal were agreeable to everyone; others proved highly ____________________.
7. If it is allowed to spread unchecked, the poison of racial prejudice will have a(n) ____________________ effect on our community.
8. Refusing to be ____________________ by her failure to find a summer job, Lucy made up her mind to try again.
9. We ____________________ such heavy casualties on the enemy that they were forced to break off the engagement and retreat.
10. Despite the fact that she has no official title, she has become the ____________________ director of the company.

End Set B

SadlierConnect.com: Interactive Word Games

Synonyms

*Choose the word or form of the word from this Unit that is the same or most nearly the same in meaning as the **boldface** word or expression in the phrase. Write that word on the line. Use a dictionary if necessary.*

1. made a **futile** effort to defeat the enemy ____________
2. **baffle** friends with his odd reaction ____________
3. given authority to **administer** punishment ____________
4. work in a **coalition** with other animal rights groups ____________
5. **recoil** at the idea of getting up so early ____________
6. a **customary** solution to the problem ____________
7. became the **operative** leader ____________
8. **obtained** a ticket to the tournament ____________
9. the **rebellious** behavior of a child ____________
10. became **dismayed** by the lack of money ____________
11. **rush** past the haunted house ____________
12. a **jester** in the king's court ____________
13. persuaded lawmakers to **repeal** the law ____________
14. would **humiliate** her friends with her shocking speech ____________
15. brought up the **debatable** issue on the Senate floor ____________

Antonyms

*Choose the word or form of the word from this Unit that is most nearly opposite in meaning to the **boldface** word or expression in the phrase. Write that word on the line. Use a dictionary if necessary.*

1. had a **benign** influence on other people ____________
2. as **dry** as the soil along the riverbed ____________
3. kept important papers in a **fireproof** safe ____________
4. gave a **lackluster** performance for the audience ____________
5. surprised by the **friendly** response from the crowd ____________

Writing: Words in Action

Imagine that you are Coyote. You have spent your life trying to trick others. You want to persuade your fellow mythical creatures that you are really doing good for the world. Write an argument to support your claim using at least two details from the passage (pages 56–57) and three or more words from this Unit.

Vocabulary in Context

Some of the words you have studied in this Unit appear in ***boldface*** *type. Read the passage below, and then circle the letter of the correct answer for each word as it is used in context.*

The Native American city of Cahokia has been called America's first city. It was situated in Illinois, along the floodplains of the Mississippi River and across from modern-day St. Louis, Missouri. Cahokia was founded roughly 1000 years ago; it thrived for 300 years, and then disappeared, leaving a **void**. The reasons for its ending are **controversial**, but a common view is that a devastating flood wiped it out. If so, the **sodden** landscape swallowed the lost city's secrets and treasures for centuries.

Greater Cahokia was a huge settlement, the largest north of Mexico. Researchers believe up to 50,000 people lived in the city at its peak—more than in London at the same time. The people of Cahokia built numerous giant earthen mounds resembling flat-topped pyramids. According to archaeologists, the tops of the mounds were used as platforms for temples and homes for elites, and they also served as burial sites for chiefs.

Researchers believe that a significant trade network existed between the inland Cahokians and coastal tribes that lived hundreds of miles away. Found artifacts such as seashells and sharks' teeth back up this theory—for how else would such maritime items end up in Illinois? Excavations have also unearthed evidence of barricades erected to guard against **malignant** outside forces. Since the barricades were made of wood, they likely were **inflammable** and would periodically have to be rebuilt.

Today, Cahokia is a World Heritage Site and the largest archaeological site in the country. Hundreds of its acres are open to visitors who want to explore and learn about this ancient city that continues to **bewilder** researchers and visitors.

---

1. **Void** comes from the Latin word **vacuus. Vacuus** most likely means

a. foundation　　**c.** collection
b. emptiness　　**d.** opportunity

2. What is the meaning of **controversial** as it is used in paragraph 1?

a. within reason　　**c.** in dispute
b. in the field of　　**d.** out of order

3. Which word means the same as **sodden** as it is used in paragraph 1?

a. slippery　　**c.** watertight
b. waterlogged　　**d.** vacant

4. What does **malignant** most likely mean as it is used in paragraph 3?

a. outlying　　**c.** deadly
b. sophisticated　　**d.** incompatible

5. In paragraph 3, what does the use of the word **inflammable** suggest about the barricades?

a. They are giant.　　**c.** They are fireproof.
b. They are wooden.　　**d.** They can catch fire.

6. The word **bewilder** means about the same as

a. mystify　　**c.** destroy
b. expand　　**d.** deteriorate

Read the following passage, taking note of the boldface words and their contexts. These words are among those you will be studying in Unit 5. It may help you to complete the exercises in this Unit if you refer to the way the words are used below.

The "Elephant Man" Is Dead

<Obituary>

Joseph Merrick, "The Elephant Man," Dies at 27
by Archibald Winsor Jorrocks for *The Sentinel*

Joseph Carey Merrick, known as the Elephant Man, died on April 11, 1890, in the London Hospital at age 27. He was cursed with extreme physical deformities caused by an unknown and incurable disease. The coroner's report lists the official cause of death as asphyxia. It was brought about by the **substantial** weight of his massive head.

Official versions, however, can be **fallible**. There is **uncertainty** surrounding this conclusion. His doctor and friend Frederick Treves believes Merrick's neck snapped as he attempted to sleep lying down. Because of his deformities, Merrick slept sitting up. Treves maintains that Merrick wanted to fulfill a simple wish to sleep like others—and that this wish cost him his life.

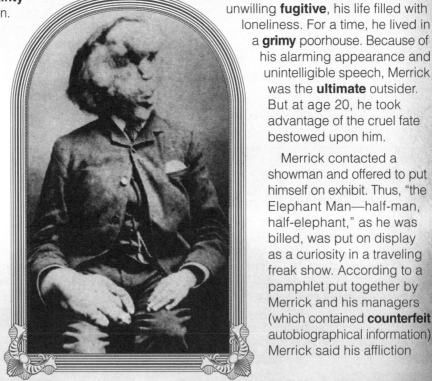

Joseph Carey Merrick, known as the Elephant Man

Joseph Merrick was born in Leicester on August 5, 1862, son of Joseph and Mary Jane Merrick. Although healthy at birth, young Joseph soon developed unsightly tumors. His lips swelled dramatically, and a large, bony lump formed on his forehead. Wart-like growths resembling cauliflowers appeared on his head and body. His feet and right hand and arm ballooned to many times the normal size. (Measurements taken at the time of death indicate his head was 36 inches in circumference, while his right wrist was 12 inches around.)

Merrick's mother died when he was 11 years old, and his father remarried. His new stepmother **dominated** the household and showed Joseph not one **iota** of kindness. The boy was cast out to fend for himself. He became an unwilling **fugitive**, his life filled with loneliness. For a time, he lived in a **grimy** poorhouse. Because of his alarming appearance and unintelligible speech, Merrick was the **ultimate** outsider. But at age 20, he took advantage of the cruel fate bestowed upon him.

Merrick contacted a showman and offered to put himself on exhibit. Thus, "the Elephant Man—half-man, half-elephant," as he was billed, was put on display as a curiosity in a traveling freak show. According to a pamphlet put together by Merrick and his managers (which contained **counterfeit** autobiographical information), Merrick said his affliction was the result of his mother being knocked down by a fairground elephant while she was pregnant. This **anecdote** was told by his family to explain his disease, and Joseph held fast to this belief.

Merrick ended up in London on display at a shop set up to host cheap entertainment. Children and adults taunted him, and cruel onlookers **mauled** him. It was here that Frederick Treves discovered him and invited him to the London Hospital for an examination.

Because the hospital did not handle incurable cases, an administrator **entreated** other institutions to offer Merrick a safe haven. When this proved fruitless, a letter to *The Times* describing Merrick's plight brought an outpouring of sympathy and financial donations.

Merrick settled into a comfortable apartment at the London Hospital. And, finally, Joseph Merrick's **radiant** intelligence, gentle nature, and true **potential** were revealed. Beneath his startling exterior, the Elephant Man was a **docile**, compassionate, intelligent soul who loved art, music, and animals. He was drawn to beauty in all forms, and society patrons visited him and gave him gifts.

To protect himself from stares and scrutiny, Joseph Merrick often wore a hat and mask in public.

The world that treated Merrick so cruelly in life treated him with respect upon his death. A memorial service was attended by doctors, nurses, royalty, actors, and artists. A fitting epitaph might be: You'll never understand a person until you walk a mile in his shoes.

Audio

For iWords and audio passages, go to **SadlierConnect.com**.

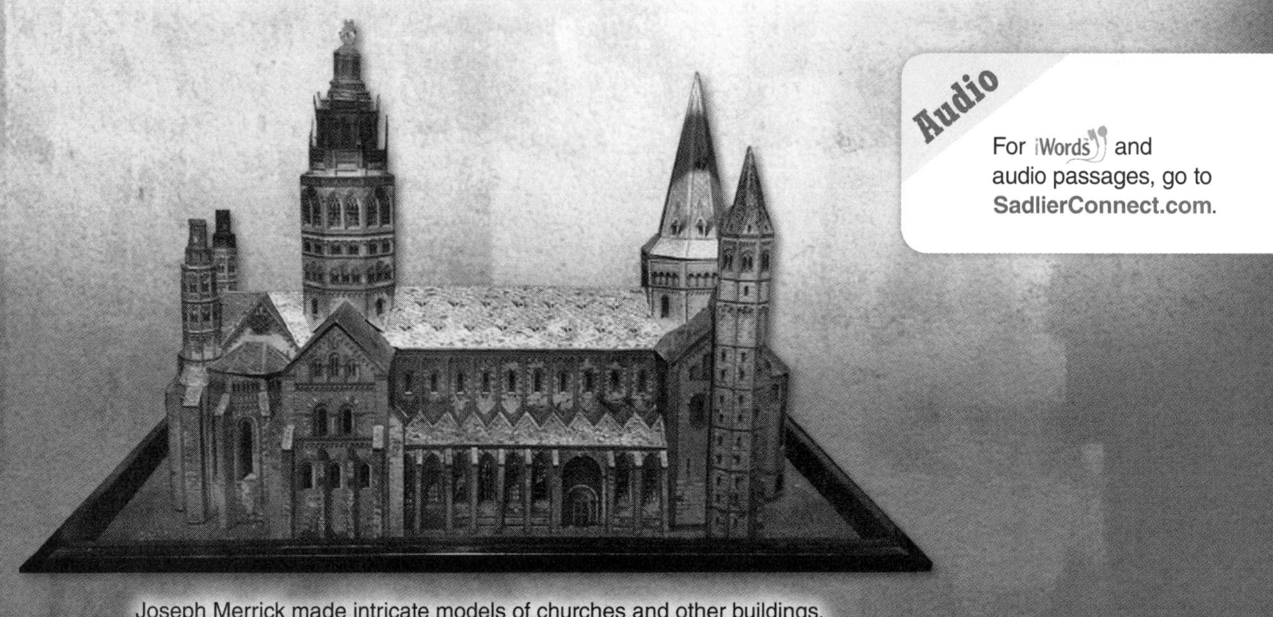

Joseph Merrick made intricate models of churches and other buildings.

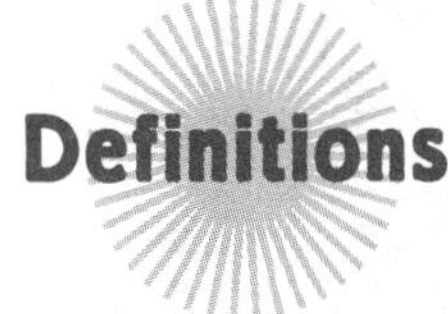

Note the spelling, pronunciation, part(s) of speech, and definition(s) of each of the following words. Then write the appropriate form of the word in the blank space in the illustrative sentence(s) following.

1. anecdote (an′ ek dōt)
(*n.*) a short account of an incident in someone's life
The governor told a humorous ____________ about her first day in office.

2. counterfeit (kau̇n′ tər fit)
(*n.*) an imitation designed to deceive; (*adj.*) not genuine, fake; (*v.*) to make an illegal copy
The painting was a ____________ of Gainsborough's *Blue Boy*.
The forger was selling ____________ postage stamps to his friends and neighbors.
It is a crime to ____________ money.

3. dominate (däm′ ə nāt)
(*v.*) to rule over by strength or power, control; to tower over, command due to height
History shows that powerful nations tend to ____________ weaker ones.

4. fallible (fal′ ə bəl)
(*adj.*) capable of being wrong, mistaken, or inaccurate
The researcher's ____________ methods led to faulty conclusions.

5. grimy (grī′ mē)
(*adj.*) very dirty, covered with dirt or soot
The miners emerged from the pits with ____________ hands and faces.

6. maul (môl)
(*v.*) to beat or knock about, handle roughly; to mangle; (*n.*) a heavy hammer
The tiger was about to ____________ its victim when the zookeeper stepped between them.

7. radiant (rā′ dē ənt)
(*adj.*) shining, bright; giving forth light or energy
A model needs to have a ____________ smile in order to advertise toothpaste.

8. substantial (səb stan′ shəl)
(*adj.*) large, important; major, significant; prosperous; not imaginary, material
Expecting a ____________ raise in salary, the employee put a down payment on a new car.

9. tactful (takt′ fəl) — (*adj.*) skilled in handling difficult situations or people, polite

A ____________________ approach is usually the wisest one to take with coworkers.

10. uncertainty (ən sər′ tən tē) — (*n.*) doubt, the state of being unsure

____________________ about the future was the immigrants' greatest concern.

*For each item, determine whether the **boldface** word from pages 70–71 makes sense in the context of the sentence. Circle the item numbers next to the six sentences in which the words are used correctly.*

1. Although the campfire had gone out, the logs were still **radiant** and burning hot.
2. After a long and **tactful** journey, the ship's passengers and crew were overjoyed at the sight of land ahead.
3. Several experts were called in to determine whether the ancient map was real or **counterfeit**.
4. In one kind of chemical change, two or more substances **dominate** to form a new substance.
5. Next summer, we will take down the little shed in the backyard and replace it with a more **substantial** structure.
6. At next week's public meeting, the parks department will review various proposals for the new skateboard park and then choose the one that is most **fallible**.
7. After we spent several hours cleaning it, the **grimy** oven looked almost new.
8. It is rare for a black bear to **maul** a human, since these animals would rather avoid people than attack them.
9. In a suspenseful story, **uncertainty** about what will happen next keeps readers both engaged and entertained.
10. The gifted student was able to solve the difficult **anecdote** in less than five minutes.

Choosing the Right Word

*Select the **boldface** word that better completes each sentence. You might refer to the passage on pages 68–69 to see how most of these words are used in context. Note that the choices might be related forms of the Unit words.*

1. Rarely in our history has one man so (**dominated, mauled**) the federal government as Franklin D. Roosevelt did during his four terms.

2. His (**anecdotes, uncertainties**) were amusing, but what did they have to do with his central topic?

3. In modern hospitals, everything possible is done to prevent mistakes resulting from human (**fallibility, uncertainty**).

4. It wasn't very (**substantial, tactful**) of you to tell her that her new eyeglasses were out of style.

5. One certain thing in life is that there will always be many (**anecdotes, uncertainties**).

6. As soon as Horace opened his lunch bag, I realized he needed something more (**grimy, substantial**) to eat.

7. Although the ideals of my youth have been (**dominated, mauled**) by hard experience, they have not been totally destroyed.

8. I suspected that his expression of happiness was (**substantial, counterfeit**) and that he was really jealous of our success.

9. One of our best hopes of solving the energy problem lies in making direct use of (**radiant, tactful**) energy from the sun.

10. There, in the very heart of the noisy and (**grimy, fallible**) city, was a truly beautiful little park.

11. At the end of the last century, one team (**mauled, dominated**) baseball and won the World Series three out of five years.

12. Although Thea always tried to say the right thing, she had to admit she was not a naturally (**tactful, grimy**) person.

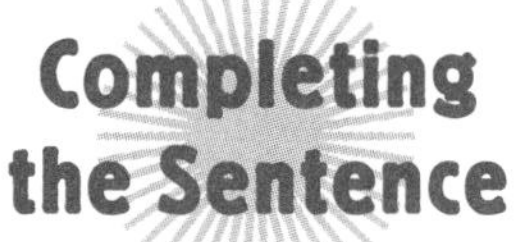

Choose the word from the word bank that best completes each of the following sentences. Write the correct word or form of the word in the space provided.

anecdote	**dominate**	**grimy**	**radiant**	**tactful**
counterfeit	**fallible**	**maul**	**substantial**	**uncertainty**

1. The windows had become so ____________________ and spotted that it took me some time to get them clean.

2. As she told us the good news, her face was ____________________ with joy.

3. There is an old saying that pencils are made with erasers because human beings are____________________.

4. The boat has been so badly ____________________ by the storm that it will have to be overhauled before it can be used again.

5. The wily old Senator had such a forceful and aggressive personality that he soon came to ____________________ his entire party.

6. Unwilling to bear the ____________________ any longer, I called the Dean of Admissions to find out if I had been admitted.

7. The new book of presidential ____________________ contains many amusing stories involving our Chief Executives, both past and present.

8. Since all our cashiers handle large sums of money, we have given them special training in recognizing ____________________ bills.

9. Despite the doctor's best efforts, there has been no ____________________ change in the patient's condition for weeks.

10. To be ____________________ in everyday life means doing whatever you can to avoid hurting the feelings of other people.

End Set A

Definitions

Note the spelling, pronunciation, part(s) of speech, and definition(s) of each of the following words. Then write the appropriate form of the word in the blank space in the illustrative sentence(s) following.

1. consolidate (kən säl′ ə dāt)
(*v.*) to combine, unite; to make solid or firm
The generals agreed to ____________________ their forces for the invasion.

2. docile (däs′ əl)
(*adj.*) easily taught, led, or managed; obedient
She was a ____________________ child, eager to learn and to please.

3. entreat (en trēt′)
(*v.*) to beg, implore, ask earnestly
The dog's eyes seemed to ____________________ me for an extra helping of dinner.

4. fickle (fik′ əl)
(*adj.*) liable to change very rapidly, erratic; marked by a lack of constancy or steadiness, inconsistent
My aunt's interests change with the weather, showing she is a truly ____________________ person.

5. fugitive (fyü′ jə tiv)
(*n.*) one who flees or runs away; (*adj.*) fleeting, lasting a very short time; wandering; difficult to grasp
That thief is a ____________________ from justice.
Mr. and Mrs. Hirsch had a few ____________________ moments together before Mrs. Hirsch boarded the train.

6. iota (ī ō′ tə)
(*n.*) a very small part or quantity
The employer had not an ____________________ of proof, but he blamed the new clerk for the theft anyway.

7. potential (pə ten′ chəl)
(*adj.*) possible, able to happen; (*n.*) something that can develop or become a reality
Hurricanes are a ____________________ threat to this area.
They were a football team with ____________________.

8. rural (rür′ əl)
(*adj.*) relating to farm areas and life in the country
They settled in a ____________________ community that was miles from the nearest large city.

9. tamper (tam′ pər) — (*v.*) to interfere with; to handle in a secret and improper way

Please don't ____________________ with our baggage.

10. ultimate (əl′ tə mət) — (*adj.*) last, final; most important or extreme; eventual; basic, fundamental

California is our ____________________ destination on this cross-country trip.

Using Context

*For each item, determine whether the **boldface** word from pages 74–75 makes sense in the context of the sentence. Circle the item numbers next to the six sentences in which the words are used correctly.*

1. Although she is generally a **docile** person, she is never afraid to speak her mind about causes she believes in.
2. The press continued to **tamper** the famous actress months after the scandal broke, causing her to file a restraining order.
3. My sister and I tried to **consolidate** all of our items into one suitcase before realizing such a thing was not feasible for a two-week-long international trip.
4. The mayor encouraged the city's residents to remain in their homes as the search for the **fugitive** began.
5. Her memory is so **fickle** that she remembers everything from the time she was a child to now.
6. There is no use worrying about all **potential** outcomes; let's just wait and see what actually happens before reacting.
7. I had hoped a vacation in the **rural** town would be relaxing, but after a few days without the amenities of a city I found myself getting antsy to leave.
8. After months of allowing his boss to **entreat** him, he decided to find a new job where he would be respected.
9. The **iota** I felt as the orchestra finished their final piece made me regret that I hadn't learned how to play an instrument.
10. My **ultimate** goal in working out is to lose weight, but I've found exercising comes with many additional benefits.

Choosing the Right Word

*Select the **boldface** word that better completes each sentence. You might refer to the passage on pages 68–69 to see how most of these words are used in context. Note that the choices might be related forms of the Unit words.*

1. Throughout the course of its history, the United States has opened its doors to (**fugitives, iota**) from tyranny in other lands.

2. Larry got good grades on the midterm tests, but he is headed for trouble because he hasn't done a(n) (**potential, iota**) of work since then.

3. To make her finances easier to manage, Mrs. Bridges decided to (**entreat, consolidate**) her two bank accounts into one.

4. If you want to see the (**iota, ultimate**) in shoe styles, ask Beth to show you the new sandals she bought for the spring dance.

5. The (**ultimate, rural**) population of the United States is growing smaller, but farms are as important as ever to the nation.

6. Evidence showed that the lawyer had tried to (**consolidate, tamper**) with the witnesses by offering them bribes to change their testimony.

7. Marisa felt a (**rural, fugitive**) glow of happiness, but it was gone in an instant.

8. Alma is such a (**fickle, potential**) fan that she starts rooting for the opposing teams when they start winning.

9. The mayor won't be reelected unless she can (**consolidate, entreat**) the groups supporting her.

10. I know from personal experience how much harm smoking can do, and I (**tamper, entreat**) you not to get started on that miserable habit.

11. The fire department found that the wiring in our kitchen was a (**potential, rural**) fire hazard.

12. The young man who seemed so quiet and (**docile, ultimate**) turned out to be very well informed and to have strong opinions of his own.

Choose the word from the word bank that best completes each of the following sentences. Write the correct word or form of the word in the space provided.

consolidate	entreat	fugitive	potential	tamper
docile	**fickle**	**iota**	**rural**	**ultimate**

1. The taste of the public is so ____________________ that a TV performer who is a big hit one year may be forgotten the next.

2. I took my car to a qualified repair shop rather than run the risk of damaging it further by ____________________ with it myself.

3. Trying desperately to avoid the police, the ____________________ hid in the cellar of the abandoned house.

4. The Board of Education believes it would save considerable money to ____________________ three small schools into one big school.

5. After living so long in a large city, I was happy to spend a few weeks in those beautiful ____________________ surroundings.

6. Though the United Nations has many lesser objectives, its ____________________ goal is to achieve lasting world peace.

7. Though Company A has very little chance of expanding in the near future, the ____________________ growth rate of Company B is staggering.

8. We discovered that there was not a(n) ____________________ of truth in the rumors that they had spread so eagerly.

9. "As a mother," the woman said to the judge, "I ____________________ you to show leniency toward my son."

10. Because I had expected the children to be hard to handle, I was pleasantly surprised by their ____________________ behavior.

End Set B

Synonyms

*Choose the word or form of the word from this Unit that is the same or most nearly the same in meaning as the **boldface** word or expression in the phrase. Write that word on the line. Use a dictionary if necessary.*

1. made a **diplomatic** remark ______________
2. moved forward without **hesitation** ______________
3. shared a charming **story** from her childhood ______________
4. **control** the software market ______________
5. reach his full **capability** ______________
6. **alter** the legal documents ______________
7. gave the **manageable** horse to the child ______________
8. the **brilliant** rays of the sun ______________
9. has an **imperfect** memory ______________
10. young prey **mangled** by a hyena ______________
11. would **beseech** me to give them money ______________
12. move over a **smidgen** ______________
13. fooled into buying the **phony** diamond ______________
14. was a **runaway** from oppression ______________
15. made **remarkable** progress last week ______________

Antonyms

*Choose the word or form of the word from this Unit that is most nearly opposite in meaning to the **boldface** word or expression in the phrase. Write that word on the line. Use a dictionary if necessary.*

1. to **separate** the members of the two clubs ______________
2. with Yellowstone National Park as the **initial** destination ______________
3. **spotless** white counters ______________
4. as **constant** as the weather ______________
5. activities influenced by the **urban** landscape ______________

Writing: Words in Action

Suppose that you are Dr. Frederick Treves. A newspaper reporter is interviewing you about what Merrick was like. Write two or three questions and answers from the interview. Make each answer at least two sentences long. Use two details from the passage (pages 68–69) and three or more words from this Unit.

Vocabulary in Context

*Some of the words you have studied in this Unit appear in **boldface** type. Read the passage below, and then circle the letter of the correct answer for each word as it is used in context.*

The London Hospital was founded in Whitechapel, East London, in 1740. It was one of five new "voluntary" hospitals created in London between 1720 and 1760. All of them were funded by wealthy philanthropists and maintained by private charities. They were each managed by an unpaid board of (non-medical) governors, and the medical staff took no payment.

Voluntary hospitals were ambitious. They treated the sick free of charge, but they also provided pioneering doctors with facilities that encouraged discovery and innovation. Voluntary hospitals were the first teaching hospitals, where students could learn from the best physicians and surgeons. In 1758, the London Hospital Medical College became the first hospital-based medical school in Britain.

The motto of the London Hospital was *Humani nihil a me alienum puto*: "Nothing that is human is alien to me." It expresses the idealism of the Enlightenment. History is **fickle**, and time and social change **tamper** with the best intentions. As the century drew to a close, so did the era of human and scientific progress that had begun over a century earlier. Ideas of civilization and human happiness were lost in the smoke of the Industrial Revolution.

Early pictures show the London Hospital in a **rural** setting. By the 1830s, Whitechapel was an industrial slum. Poverty, crime, and disease thrived in its maze of **grimy** alleyways. Epidemics are not **tactful** in their demands for attention. Hospital wards were overcrowded, and surgery was often fatal. Antiseptic cleanliness was unknown. Whitechapel's germs began to **consolidate** forces, and the hospital itself became a breeding-house of disease.

---

1. What is the meaning of **fickle** as it is used in paragraph 3?

a. humorous **c.** changeable
b. unhelpful **d.** incomprehensible

2. In paragraph 3, what does the use of **tamper** suggest about time and social change?

a. They are destructive. **c.** They are unpredictable.
b. They are playful. **d.** They are thieves.

3. **Rural** comes from the Latin word **rūs**. **Rūs** most likely means

a. suburb **c.** countryside
b. river **d.** woodland

4. The word **grimy** means about the same as

a. hideous **c.** terrifying
b. dark **d.** filthy

5. Which word means the same as **tactful** as it is used in paragraph 4?

a. urgent **c.** clear
b. courteous **d.** frequent

6. What does the word **consolidate** most likely mean as it is used in paragraph 4?

a. oppose **c.** strengthen
b. abandon **d.** combine

UNIT 6

Read the following passage, taking note of the ***boldface*** *words and their contexts. These words are among those you will be studying in Unit 6. It may help you to complete the exercises in this Unit if you refer to the way the words are used below.*

Nazca Lines

<Persuasive Essay>

If one **browses** the list of more than 900 locations the United Nations has identified as World Heritage Sites, none remains more mysterious than the Nazca Lines of southwest Peru.

These lines, sometimes called geoglyphs, are giant ground drawings. They cover an area of nearly 200 square miles. In the dry, windless climate of the high desert plain, the drawings have survived for many centuries. The huge shapes, **prominent** from the air, first attracted world attention in the 1920s, when airplane pilots reported these unique and **inimitable** creations.

Some of the lines depict geometric shapes, such as trapezoids, triangles, and spirals. Others show gigantic animals and plants. One geoglyph of a monkey, for example, measures 360 feet long; while a bird resembling a condor stretches 440 feet.

Who were the **anonymous** designers of these shapes?

How were the geoglyphs made, and why? For nearly a century, experts have been in a lively, **dynamic** debate. They have done their **utmost** to explain a phenomenon that still **frustrates** rational explanation.

For many years, the German-born mathematician and archaeologist Maria Reiche **prescribed** the prevailing view on the Nazca Lines. Reiche argued that the lines were a giant sun calendar and astronomical observatory. Systematic investigation by the British astronomer Gerald Hawkins, however, dislodged this theory, even if it did not thoroughly **eradicate** it. Critics of Hawkins, in turn, have pointed out that he paid only **marginal** attention to the cultural context of the Nazca Lines. Hawkins has also been criticized for employing only a **makeshift** network of astronomical targets, a selection that would make more sense in England than in the Southern Hemisphere. Thus, Hawkins

A monkey depiction in the Nazca Lines is 360 feet long

may have only scratched the surface of the astronomical significance of the Nazca Lines.

The Reiche-Hawkins debate, at least, has unfolded on a sober playing field. Some theorists of Nazca, however, have not been **reluctant** to offer explanations that may fairly be described as **quaint**.

Among the most eccentric theories is one that says the lines functioned as actual runways. One imaginative theorist, for example, was convinced that the drawings were meant to be seen from the air. He argued that the creators of the lines also managed to build hot-air balloons, which they used to admire their handiwork from aloft.

Another even more imaginative commentator has proposed that the "runways" of Nazca were not used for takeoffs, but for landings. According to this theory, the inbound passengers were space aliens. After they landed, they intermarried with earthlings. Was this theory deliberately intended to **dupe** the public? Perhaps it was, since its principal proponent **previewed** his ideas in a highly profitable best-selling book.

The puzzles of the Nazca Lines are far from being solved. Among the **pending** theories, perhaps the most persuasive claims that the lines had a religious purpose. According to this theory, ancient people walked the lines as pilgrims. These people worshipped mountain deities, largely because water came down from the mountains. For all cultures, water has a central role. The origin, movement, and function of water were subjects of fundamental importance. It may be, then, that the Nazca Lines, which are so much more visible from the air than from ground level, were designed to be pilgrimage routes for people worshipping the water-giving deities of the mountains. This is the most feasible and convincing answer to the puzzle of the Nazca Lines.

An aerial view of a bird representation in the Nazca Lines

Audio

For iWords and audio passages, go to **SadlierConnect.com**.

Note the spelling, pronunciation, part(s) of speech, and definition(s) of each of the following words. Then write the appropriate form of the word in the blank space in the illustrative sentence(s) following.

1. anonymous (ə nän′ ə məs)
(*adj.*) unnamed, without the name of the person involved (writer, composer, etc.); unknown; lacking individuality

The detective received an ____________________ tip that helped to narrow the search for the thief.

2. dupe (düp)
(*n.*) a person easily tricked or deceived; (*v.*) to deceive

He played the ____________________ in one of Shakespeare's comedies.

The villain in the play tried to ____________________ the hero out of his money.

3. eradicate (i rad′ ə kāt)
(*v.*) to root out, get rid of, destroy completely

The team of doctors and researchers worked tirelessly to ____________________ the disease.

4. inimitable (in im′ ə tə bəl)
(*adj.*) not capable of being copied or imitated

The young performer stole the show with her ____________________ charm.

5. makeshift (māk′ shift)
(*n.*) a temporary substitute for something else; (*adj.*) crude, flimsy, or temporary

The boards and cinder blocks are only a ____________________ until the bookcase arrives.

The cot serves as a ____________________ bed for guests.

6. pending (pen′ diŋ)
(*adj.*) waiting to be settled; (*prep.*) until

Curiosity about the ____________________ trial builds daily.

Sentencing of the criminal was postponed ____________________ the judge's decision.

7. preview (prē′ vyü)
(*n.*) something seen in advance; (*v.*) to view beforehand

The critics saw a ____________________ of the new movie.

The teacher decided to ____________________ the video before showing it to the class.

8. quaint (kwānt)
(*adj.*) odd or old-fashioned in a pleasing way; clever, ingenious; skillfully made

My parents stayed at a ____________________ old inn in Stowe, Vermont.

9. scrimp (skrimp)
(*v.*) to handle very economically or stingily; to supply in a way that is small, short, or scanty
When the factory closed and other work was scarce, many people were forced to ________________.

10. utmost (ət′ most)
(*adj.*) greatest, highest, farthest; (*n.*) the extreme limit
The voters had the ________________ regard for her ability as a leader.

Using Context

*For each item, determine whether the **boldface** word from pages 82–83 makes sense in the context of the sentence. Circle the item numbers next to the six sentences in which the words are used correctly.*

1. The lead guitar player's style is **inimitable**, so it's impossible to imagine how the band could ever replace him.
2. If we get too close to the deer, it will **scrimp** and then disappear into the woods.
3. In one of Aesop's many fables, a sly fox finds a way to **dupe** a raven out of a tasty piece of cheese.
4. The police officers assured the storeowner that they would do their **utmost** to find the shoplifter whose image appeared on the security cameras.
5. If we want to make it to the state championships this year, we will have to seriously **eradicate** our skills.
6. I thought it was very clever of you to turn a clean plastic garbage bag into a **makeshift** rain poncho that would keep you dry during the sudden downpour.
7. The **pending** event happened so long ago that they are no longer feeling its effects.
8. The newspaper reporter refused to reveal the identity of the **anonymous** source she had quoted in her story about the town's corruption to anyone but her editor.
9. At the end of this bestselling novel, readers will find a 15-page **preview** of the author's next work.
10. All day long, I found myself feeling **quaint** and nauseated, and now I am wondering if I am coming down with the flu.

Choosing the Right Word

*Select the **boldface** word that better completes each sentence. You might refer to the passage on pages 80–81 to see how most of these words are used in context. Note that the choices might be related forms of the Unit words.*

1. The exhibition at the fair was intended to give visitors a (**preview, dupe**) of what life might be like in twenty years.
2. You must realize that, although we may find the customs of other lands (**anonymous, quaint**), they are just part of everyday life in those areas.
3. The new parking regulations are only a (**dupe, makeshift**) that will have to be replaced by a better plan within a few years.
4. Although we cannot mention her by name, we want to express our heartfelt gratitude to the (**quaint, anonymous**) donor who gave us this generous gift.
5. (**Pending, Eradicating**) the outcome of the national election, none of the foreign governments is willing to take any definite action.
6. He still doesn't realize that he has been used as a (**dupe, makeshift**) by our opponents to do their dirty work for them.
7. It is very easy to say that our city government should (**scrimp, eradicate**) to balance its budget, but which departments should spend less?
8. It is wise to (**dupe, preview**) the contents of a book before you buy it.
9. Landing a man on the moon was a great achievement, but it is far from being the (**utmost, pending**) limit of our space program.
10. Even before we saw Alice, we heard her (**inimitable, anonymous**) high-pitched giggle and knew she was at the party.
11. After the big hurricane destroyed our homes, many of us lived in (**pending, makeshift**) shelters.
12. Nothing can (**eradicate, scrimp**) the love of liberty from the hearts of a free people!

Completing the Sentence

Choose the word from the word bank that best completes each of the following sentences. Write the correct word or form of the word in the space provided.

anonymous	**eradicate**	**makeshift**	**preview**	**scrimp**
dupe	**inimitable**	**pending**	**quaint**	**utmost**

1. Safety measures are of the ________________ importance when you are planning a canoe trip over rivers filled with dangerous rapids.

2. Although we know who wrote such famous epics as the *Aeneid* and the *Iliad*, the author of *Beowulf* remains ________________.

3. Many books have been written about boys, but none of them can match the ________________ qualities in the tales of Tom Sawyer and Huckleberry Finn.

4. Each unit in the textbook opens with a section that ________________ the chapter materials.

5. When we visited Salem, Massachusetts, last year, we were charmed by the ________________ eighteenth-century houses in the town.

6. The suspect was held in the local police station, ________________ the outcome of the investigation.

7. For months I ________________ on everything to save enough money to buy the replacement tires for my bicycle.

8. We may not be able to ________________ crime in our community, but if we go about it in the right way, I am sure we can reduce it greatly.

9. When unexpected guests turned up on the doorstep, I hurriedly made a few ________________ arrangements to accommodate them.

10. I was ________________ into trusting him, and I have paid a heavy price for being misled so easily.

End Set A

Definitions

Note the spelling, pronunciation, part(s) of speech, and definition(s) of each of the following words. Then write the appropriate form of the word in the blank space in the illustrative sentence(s) following.

1. **browse** (braüz) — (*v.*) to nibble, graze; to read casually; to window-shop

   I like to ____________________ through a book before deciding to buy it.

2. **dynamic** (dī nam′ ik) — (*adj.*) active, energetic, forceful

   The social network was looking to hire a creative person with a ____________________ personality.

3. **frustrate** (frəs′ trāt) — (*v.*) to prevent from accomplishing a purpose or fulfilling a desire; to cause feelings of discouragement

   Nothing could ____________________ our plans to storm the fort.

4. **grim** (grim) — (*adj.*) stern, merciless; fierce, savage, cruel

   Millions of poor people face the ____________________ prospect of hunger.

5. **marginal** (märj′ ən əl) — (*adj.*) in, at, or near the edge or margin; only barely good, large, or important enough for the purpose

   During times of economic hardship, many people have only a ____________________ standard of living.

6. **prescribe** (pri skrīb′) — (*v.*) to order as a rule or course to be followed; to order for medical purposes

   The doctor was quick to ____________________ complete bed rest.

7. **prominent** (präm′ ə nənt) — (*adj.*) standing out so as to be easily seen; important, well-known

   Some famous authors are ____________________ figures in society.

8. **reluctant** (ri lək′ tənt) — (*adj.*) unwilling, holding back

   The attorney called the ____________________ witness to the stand.

9. snare (snâr)
(*v.*) to trap, catch; (*n.*) a trap or entanglement

They set a trap to ____________ the rodents that were getting into the garden.

The unsuspecting spy was caught in a ____________ set by the other side.

10. vengeance (ven′ jəns)
(*n.*) punishment in return for an injury or a wrong; unusual force or violence

History is filled with examples of violent rulers taking ____________ on their enemies.

Using Context

*For each item, determine whether the **boldface** word from pages 86–87 makes sense in the context of the sentence. Circle the item numbers next to the six sentences in which the words are used correctly.*

1. His **grim** acceptance of the news that he did not get the job demonstrated how resilient he truly is.
2. I feel such **vengeance** for the subject of art history that more than once I've found myself dozing off during a lecture.
3. The prosecuting attorney tried to **browse** the suspect into admitting she was lying about her alibi, but she never strayed from her story.
4. His fear of flying is a **snare** that prevents him from seeing all that the world has to offer.
5. He has such a **marginal** passion for helping others that it's no wonder he started his own nonprofit to aid those in need around the world.
6. I was **reluctant** to share my project for the science fair with anyone in case they decided to steal the idea for themselves.
7. After weeks of feeling ill, I was grateful to find a doctor who could quickly diagnose my problem and **prescribe** me the medication that would improve my health.
8. The new English teacher was an instant favorite due to her **dynamic** way of teaching, which helped even the most indifferent students become excited about literature.
9. While I do not approve of your plan, I will not attempt to **frustrate** your efforts to carry it out.
10. The entire graduating class was thrilled that such a **prominent** author would speak at their commencement ceremony.

Choosing the Right Word

*Select the **boldface** word that better completes each sentence. You might refer to the passage on pages 80–81 to see how most of these words are used in context. Note that the choices might be related forms of the Unit words.*

1. We have many good musicians in our school orchestra, but they need a (**reluctant, dynamic**) conductor to make them play as a unit.

2. His reference to a "historic downfall" after I had failed the history test struck me as a rather (**dynamic, grim**) joke.

3. Although the announcement had promised us "a (**prominent, reluctant**) speaker," she turned out to be a minor public official.

4. "Try as they may, they will never (**prescribe, snare**) me!" said the thief just before he was caught.

5. I understand your (**reluctance, vengeance**) to be our candidate in the next election, but I think it is your duty to accept the nomination.

6. The wily champion used every tennis trick she knew to (**frustrate, snare**) her opponent's attempt to come to the net and hit a winner.

7. My job is only (**marginal, prominent**); if business falls off a little, my employer might let me go.

8. For months the winter was unusually mild, but when the cold weather finally came, it struck with a (**vengeance, prominence**).

9. The mistaken idea that the most important thing in life is to "have fun" is a (**snare, vengeance**) that leads to trouble for many people.

10. To improve your unsatisfactory school record, I would (**browse, prescribe**) regular doses of study, to be taken every day for as long as is necessary.

11. As I was (**frustrating, browsing**) my way lazily through the newspaper, I was shocked to see my own name in a headline!

12. The young horse was (**frustrating, reluctant**) to cross the stream until he saw the rest of the herd do so.

Completing the Sentence

Choose the word from the word bank that best completes each of the following sentences. Write the correct word or form of the word in the space provided.

browse	**frustrate**	**marginal**	**prominent**	**snare**
dynamic	**grim**	**prescribe**	**reluctant**	**vengeance**

1. There is quite a contrast between the ____________________ administration that now runs that country and the "do-nothing" regime that preceded it.

2. Instead of seeking personal ____________________ for the wrong that has been done to you, why don't you look for justice under the law?

3. When we saw the ____________________ expression on the poor man's face, we realized that the situation was indeed serious.

4. After the angler ____________________ the fish, he unhooked it from his line and threw it back into the stream.

5. After several unsuccessful attempts to catch the waiter's eye, I became more than a little____________________.

6. It took the pharmacist about an hour to prepare the medicine that the doctor had ____________________ for my illness.

7. Is there any sight in the world more restful than cows ____________________ in a meadow alongside a little brook?

8. The most ____________________ feature of the skyline of that little town in Iowa is the four-story grain elevator.

9. The eyewitness was ____________________ to tell the police all that she had seen, but we convinced her that it was the only right thing to do.

10. I like to write ____________________ notes in a book alongside important material, but I never do so unless the book belongs to me.

End Set B

Synonyms

*Choose the word or form of the word from this Unit that is the same or most nearly the same in meaning as the **boldface** word or expression in the phrase. Write that word on the line. Use a dictionary if necessary.*

1. was of **minimal** help to the team ______________
2. a Valentine's Day note from an **unidentified** sender ______________
3. his **incomparable** way of telling a joke ______________
4. **hoodwinked** us out of our money ______________
5. a **picturesque** home based on colonial times ______________
6. got an **early glimpse** of the new spring clothing ______________
7. put the **stopgap** solution in place ______________
8. gave a **powerful** performance ______________
9. **hesitant** to walk through the haunted house ______________
10. tried her **best** to score the winning point ______________
11. wanted to **wipe out** poverty ______________
12. **baffled** by all the rules of the new game ______________
13. an issue that is still **undecided** ______________
14. **skim through** the magazine to look at the pictures ______________
15. waited to hear what the doctor would **recommend** ______________

Antonyms

*Choose the word or form of the word from this Unit that is most nearly opposite in meaning to the **boldface** word or expression in the phrase. Write that word on the line. Use a dictionary if necessary.*

1. responded with **forgiveness** to their actions ______________
2. heard the **pleasant** news on the radio ______________
3. remained a **little-known** playwright ______________
4. had to **spend** money on food and clothing ______________
5. decided to **release** the tiger ______________

Writing: Words in Action

Write a brief essay in which you describe a mysterious place that you know of and explain what makes it strange and unusual. Suggest possible explanations for the characteristics that make the place "mysterious." Include examples from your observations, studies, and reading (pages 80–81). Use three or more words from this Unit.

*Some of the words you have studied in this Unit appear in **boldface** type. Read the passage below, and then circle the letter of the correct answer for each word as it is used in context.*

In 2005 archaeologists using remote sensing equipment at prehistoric Fort Ancient Earthworks in Warren County, Ohio, found something unexpected. Underneath a large earth mound was the site of a "woodhenge," a triple ring of hundreds of tall timber posts. These posts were erected by the Native American Hopewell culture about 2,000 years ago. Since that discovery, excavators have been doing their **utmost** to learn more about this site, formally called the Moorehead Circle.

Fort Ancient is a massive enclosed hilltop earthwork that was a place of ritual and ceremony for the Hopewell. It is now a popular archaeological park. But financial resources aren't always available to pay for field research. At times, administrators of the park have had to **scrimp** and save to showcase their culturally significant site. And asking for money to develop and protect **quaint** historical landmarks can be unpleasant and **grim**. However, with public donations and a grant from Save America's Treasures, archaeologists found the woodhenge and have been digging with a **vengeance**.

The Moorehead Circle is a fascinating mystery that might require plenty of detective work to solve. So far, it has raised more questions than answers. Researchers are hoping to **snare** more clues about Native Ohioans and Ohio's own woodhenge (so-called because it reminds people of Britain's famous Stonehenge). They believe that, like Stonehenge, the large concentric circles were likely used to mark events such as the summer solstice. Whatever the true purpose of the circular structure, it took impressive strength and determination to build!

---

1. What is the meaning of **utmost** as it is used in paragraph 1?

a. development **c.** best
b. ability **d.** knowledge

2. Which word means the same as **scrimp** as it is used in paragraph 2?

a. economize **c.** consume
b. exhaust **d.** splurge

3. The word **quaint** means about the same as

a. small **c.** popular
b. picturesque **d.** regional

4. What is the meaning of **grim** as it is used in paragraph 2?

a. tough **c.** tiring
b. time-consuming **d.** dreadful

5. The word **vengeance** means about the same as

a. unusual force **c.** reliable plans
b. great care **d.** sturdy equipment

6. What does the word **snare** most likely mean as it is used in paragraph 3?

a. release **c.** catch
b. satisfy **d.** sow

Vocabulary for Comprehension

Part 1

*Read "Totem Poles," which contains words in **boldface** that appear in Units 4–6. Then answer the questions.*

Totem Poles

Among the most prominent objects of Native American material culture are totem poles. Tall, imposing, and carved from cedar wood, totem poles were created by the tribes and clans of the Northwest coast of the United States and Canada. These groups include the Tlingit, the Kwakiutl, the Haida, and the Upper Salish. Totem poles serve a variety of purposes and have substantial variety in appearance.

On the Northwest Coast, the year was divided into two seasons: summer and winter. Summer was a time of intense economic activity. Nets were cast for salmon, the region's principal resource. Native Americans also pursued other species of fish as well as a broad range of sea mammals. They used hooks, arrows, and harpoons. Women gathered shellfish and wild vegetables. Great supplies of food and skins were accumulated. When winter arrived, this activity gave way to cheerful ceremony and **spirited** feasting. At the feast, wealth was paraded and distributed to invited guests in a ritual known as the *potlatch.* This was the setting in which totem poles were commissioned, carved, and raised.

It is mistakenly assumed that totem poles tell a story. Some poles do contain narrative elements, referring to important events and memorable **anecdotes** in the life of a family or clan. But most poles advertised the owners' prosperity and social importance. Totem poles served to consolidate and signify a group's status in the community. They were the **ultimate** badge of dignity and respectability.

The word *totem* refers to a guardian or ancestral being that is often supernatural. Totems may thus be understood as a type of family crest. A helpful comparison might be the coats of arms adopted by the nobility of Europe. As the word *pole* implies, such decorative images were mounted vertically. Most totem poles ranged between 10 to 60 feet and were often carved of cedar, which was abundant in the region. Cedar has several advantages. It is soft, straight-grained, and relatively durable. Given the moist climate of the Northwest Coast, however, it was rare for a totem pole to last for more than 70 years.

There were at least a half dozen different categories of totem poles. Poles functioned as memorials, tokens of welcome and practical architectural elements, serving as house posts or as doorways. Some poles were carved in a mocking or satirical spirit, intended to **mortify** opponents or enemies. Above all, totem poles were **virtual** statements about group membership and identity.

Totem poles reached their peak of popularity in the early to mid-1800s, when wealth and prosperity in the region flourished. This is not surprising, since a clan or tribe had to enjoy a certain degree of wealth in order to procure the services of an artist or carver. After a slow and steady decline, totem poles have shown renewed **potential** in the years since the 1950s. A number of new totem poles have been commissioned for museums, parks, and international exhibitions. This highly respected art may be coming back to life!

1. As it is used in line 23, what does the word **spirited** mean?
   A) lively
   B) ghostly
   C) restrained
   D) influential

2. Which word means the same as **anecdotes** in line 32?
   A) tales
   B) leaders
   C) speeches
   D) oaths

3. **Part A**
   Based on the passage, what inference can you make about the summer season on the Northwest Coast?
   A) It was a time of leisurely relaxation.
   B) It was a time of quiet meditation.
   C) It was a time of bittersweet nostalgia.
   D) It was a time of bustling hard work.

   Part B
   Which detail from "Totem Poles" provides the **best** evidence for the answer to the previous question?
   A) "the year was divided into two seasons: summer and winter" (lines 11–13)
   B) "Summer was a time of intense economic activity." (lines 13–14)
   C) "They used hooks, arrows, and harpoons" (lines 18–19)
   D) "When winter arrived this activity gave way to cheerful ceremony " (lines 21–23)

4. What is the meaning of **ultimate** as it is used in line 37?
   A) moderate
   B) effective
   C) accessible
   D) most important

5. Which of the following **best** states the main idea of lines 29–38?
   A) Totem poles usually tell a story in chronological order.
   B) Mythical elements are typically present in totem pole decoration.
   C) The main purpose of totem poles is to proclaim a group's social status.
   D) It is extremely difficult to determine the meaning of totem poles.

6. What does the word **mortify** most likely mean as it is used in line 60?
   A) humiliate
   B) invigorate
   C) extend
   D) entertain

7. As it is used in line 62, what does the word **virtual** suggest about the totem poles?
   A) They had a deeper meaning.
   B) They acted as a statement.
   C) They were easy to remember.
   D) They were very valuable.

8. Which word means the same as **potential** in the line 72?
   A) vandalism
   B) regret
   C) possibility
   D) neglect

9. In lines 75–76 of "Totem Poles," what tone does the phrase **highly respected art** convey?
   A) admiration
   B) disgust
   C) anticipation
   D) distaste

10. Which of the following **best** identifies the primary purpose of the passage?
    A) to explain why totem pole popularity peaked in the early to mid-1800s
    B) to provide a brief survey of the significance and history of totem poles
    C) to compare and contrast the peoples of the Northwest Coast
    D) to support the claim that totem poles are similar to coats of arms

Vocabulary for Comprehension Part 2

Read these passages, which contain words in ***boldface*** *that appear in Units 4–6. Then choose the best answer to each question based on what is stated or implied in the passage(s). You may refer to the passages as often as necessary.*

Passage 1

Anyone who aspires to be a journalist, whether in traditional media such as print newspapers and magazines or newer formats such as blogs and video documentaries, needs good research and writing skills. A good investigative journalist, however, needs even more.

In this kind of journalism, a writer might dig into subjects ranging from a **counterfeiting** ring to the wrongdoings of a corrupt and **malignant** government to patterns of racial discrimination or other social injustices. To do an effective job, he or she needs to **procure** the skills of an effective storyteller and an ace detective. In some cases, he or she must also be as aggressive as a wilderness explorer or as **tactful** as a diplomat

As important as curiosity and boldness are for this profession, these qualities must also be balanced by patience and persistence. Often, investigative journalists must slog through masses of public records and other data. Also, they must be completely thorough in their fact-checking and verify every detail. After all, the most eye-opening story is **fruitless** if it is not absolutely accurate.

Passage 2

At a time when it was hardly customary for women to work outside of the home, much less pen writings that would shape public opinion, the **inimitable** Nelly Bly was a **dynamic** writer whose newspaper reporting brought about important social changes. During a career that spanned the late 1800s, Bly worked for several major newspapers and became known for bold investigative reports that shocked readers and culminated in calls for social reform. For example, for one article, she acted as if she were mentally ill so she could be put in a mental hospital and report on the **grim** abuses that took place there. For another, she posed as a thief so she could be arrested and report on how badly female prisoners were treated.

Bly's résumé, however, did not consist only of hard-hitting stories designed to **eradicate** injustice. In 1889, she set a remarkable challenge for herself— to beat the fictional hero of author Jules Verne's popular novel *Around the World in Eighty Days*. She succeeded, traveling by ship, train, horse, and balloon, and making a comparable around-the-world trip in 72 days.

1. As it is used in line 11, "malignant" most nearly means
A) unproductive.
B) aggressive.
C) malicious.
D) traditional.

2. According to the author of Passage 1, a good investigative journalist is
A) no longer necessary.
B) careless.
C) courageous and clever.
D) an unusual career for a woman.

3. As it is used in line 27, "fruitless" is closest in meaning to
A) inaccurate.
B) lively.
C) interesting.
D) useless.

4. In Passage 2, the author includes a description of Nelly Bly's around-the-world trip in order to
A) show a different side of her professional life.
B) suggest that she was not a serious investigative journalist.
C) provide another example of her concern with social injustice.
D) convince readers that it was her most important achievement.

5. What is the meaning of the word "inimitable" as it is used in line 32?
A) matchless
B) fearless
C) excitable
D) dreadful

6. As it is used in line 49, "eradicate" most nearly means
A) reject.
B) abolish.
C) weaken.
D) report.

7. How would the author of Passage 1 most likely view Bly's methods for getting a story?
A) The author of Passage 1 would consider Bly's methods of reporting too risky.
B) The author of Passage 1 would consider Bly an excellent investigative journalist.
C) The author of Passage 1 would say that Bly lacked the courage to be an investigative journalist.
D) The author of Passage 1 would say that Bly's methods would not be successful with newer formats, such as blogs.

8. Which statement best expresses the overall relationship between Passage 1 and Passage 2?
A) The purpose of Passage 1 is to inform; the purpose of Passage 2 is to entertain.
B) Passage 1 expresses a positive view toward the field of investigative journalism; Passage 2 expresses a negative view toward it.
C) Passage 1 is factual; Passage 2 is fictional.
D) Passage 1 conveys general information; Passage 2 conveys specific examples and actual events.

9. In Passage 1, the author states that investigative journalists might have to be fearless or sneaky. In Passage 2, the author demonstrates that in the course of doing her job Nelly Bly exhibited
A) sneakiness.
B) fearlessness.
C) both sneakiness and fearlessness.
D) neither sneakiness nor fearlessness.

10. Which choice provides the best evidence for the answer to the previous question?
A) Lines 35–40 ("During …social reform")
B) Lines 44–46 ("For another…treated")
C) Lines 47–49 ("Bly's …injustice")
D) Lines 53–56 ("She …in 72 days")

REVIEW UNITS 4–6

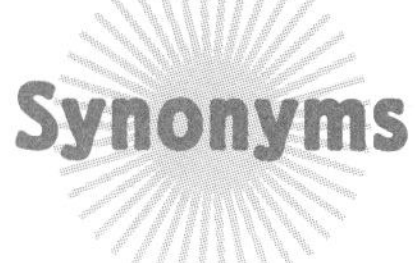

From the word bank below, choose the word that has the same or nearly the same meaning as the **boldface** word in each sentence and write it on the line. You will not use all of the words.

alliance	grim	makeshift	rural
browse	grimy	pending	sodden
docile	inflammable	prescribe	spirited
dupe	iota	radiant	tamper

1. A wild animal, such as a bear or a tiger, cannot be expected to act in a **pliant** matter. ____________

2. Over 20 theater groups in the city have formed a **coalition** in order to share resources and attract new audiences. ____________

3. The cartoon character with the **excitable** personality was always shaking his fist and stamping his feet. ____________

4. The mayor has hired an engineer to **specify** the kind of work that is needed to make the playground safe. ____________

5. We couldn't wait to take off our shoes because they had become completely **saturated**. ____________

6. My aunt sold her apartment in the city and moved to a **pastoral** area because she wanted a simpler, more peaceful kind of life. ____________

7. In my opinion, this recipe for guacamole is exactly right, and there is no need to **mess** with it. ____________

8. It can be fun to **scan** the selection of items in a catalogue or on a Web site, even if you are not planning to buy anything. ____________

9. The advertisements promised that the detergent would get clothes clean, no matter how **soiled** they might be. ____________

10. Do most science fiction stories depict a **frightful** future? ____________

11. We all agreed to disagree, since none of us wanted to see our **lively** discussion turn into an unpleasant argument. ____________

12. This food truck in the parking lot will act as a **stopgap** while the restaurant is being repaired after the fire. ____________

Select the pair of words that best completes the meaning of each of the following sentences.

1. The book is full of highly amusing stories involving many people who were ____________ at the time. One of these witty little ____________ tells how a famous director once used glue to get an actor to stand on his mark.
   a. dominant … snares
   b. prominent … anecdotes
   c. utmost … previews
   d. inimitable … iotas

2. Come to my island, and you won't be sorry! It's a ____________ paradise, with clean air, clear blue water, ____________ blue skies, five miles of white sand beaches, and the friendliest people you'll ever meet.
   a. fugitive … wayward
   b. tactful … potential
   c. virtual … radiant
   d. fickle … substantial

3. Despite setbacks that would have ____________ a less determined or ambitious person, she continued to do her ____________ to become the top tennis player in the world. As she herself admitted, she knew that she wouldn't succeed unless she gave the task her "very best shot."
   a. disheartened … utmost
   b. mortified … potential
   c. entreated … ultimate
   d. frustrated … virtual

4. "His methods are hardly what I'd call ____________, but they do get results," the sales manager remarked about her star salesperson. "If he took a more traditional approach when dealing with customers, the company's profits might not be so ____________."
   a. controversial … tactful
   b. orthodox … substantial
   c. quaint … marginal
   d. dynamic … disheartening

5. I know that an injection of procaine doesn't normally ____________ a great deal of pain. Still, the mere thought of the dentist's sharp needle is enough to make me ____________ in imaginary discomfort.
   a. eradicate … maul
   b. procure … scrimp
   c. consolidate … scurry
   d. inflict … wince

6. Two convicts escaped from the state prison last week. The police managed to recapture one of the ____________ in a matter of hours. Yet their efforts to catch the other have so far proved ____________.
   a. fugitives … fruitless
   b. dupes … wayward
   c. counterfeits … void
   d. buffoons … fallible

7. "The president's new economic program has stirred up a good deal of ____________ on Capitol Hill," the reporter observed. "Some members of Congress favor the plan; others are definitely ____________ to it."
   a. bewilderment … malignant
   b. uncertainty … reluctant
   c. vengeance … anonymous
   d. controversy … hostile

Denotation and Connotation

A word's **denotation** is its dictionary meaning, which conveys a neutral tone. The **connotation** of a word is its emotional association. Connotations may be positive, negative, or neutral.

Connotations are informal, implied meanings. We know, for example, that there is a shade of difference in meaning between *worried* and *anxious*, even though the words have similar denotations. Consider these synonyms for the neutral word *country*:

rural *rustic* *backwoods* *countrified*

Rural and *rustic* have positive connotations, suggesting the peaceful countryside, while *backwoods* and *countrified* have negative connotations, suggesting roughness and a lack of sophistication.

Look at these examples of words that are similar in denotation but have different connotations.

NEUTRAL	POSITIVE	NEGATIVE
oversee	**govern**	**dominate**
important	**prominent**	**conspicuous**
economize	**save**	**scrimp**

Expressing the Connotation

Read each sentence. Select the word in parentheses that better expresses the connotation (positive, negative, or neutral) given at the beginning of the sentence.

negative **1.** Mr. Jacobs likes to tell (**anecdotes, tales**) about his adventures.

neutral **2.** A (**changeable, fickle**) friend is often not there when you need help.

positive **3.** The speaker's use of video and audio made for a(n) (**interesting, dynamic**) presentation.

neutral **4.** The third-graders built a (**rickety, makeshift**) fort out of branches.

positive **5.** My parents ate at a (**quaint, strange**) old restaurant where there was no written menu.

negative **6.** After two inches of rain, the golf course was (**wet, sodden**).

positive **7.** Willie is so (**easygoing, docile**) that anyone can convince him to do his or her bidding.

negative **8.** Turning the corner, we came face-to-face with a crowd of people wearing (**serious, grim**) expressions.

Classical Roots

scrib, scribe, script— to write

This Latin root appears in **prescribe** (page 86). Literally "to write before," *prescribe* means "to set down as a rule, order for medical treatment, or give medical advice." Some other words based on the same root are listed below.

circumscribe	**inscription**	**proscribe**	**subscribe**
indescribable	**postscript**	**script**	**transcribe**

From the list of words above, choose the one that corresponds to each of the brief definitions below. Write the word in the blank space in the illustrative sentence below the definition. Use a dictionary if necessary.

1. to outlaw, forbid, prohibit; to banish
Building codes ____________________ that type of flimsy construction.

2. an addition to a letter written after the writer's name has been signed
The ____________________ she added to her letter was so long that it took up an entire page.

3. that which is written on a monument, coin, building; a dedication in a book
The ____________________ on the monument is short and to the point.

4. beyond description
The joy the winning team felt was ____________________.

5. handwriting; a manuscript of a play or movie
The actor read the ____________________ before he agreed to star in the new action movie.

6. to sign one's name; to express agreement or approval; to promise to take or to pay for
My parents ____________________ to several newspapers and magazines.

7. to write out or make a typewritten copy of; to write in another alphabet
The assistant will need to ____________________ her shorthand notes before inputting the information in her computer.

8. to draw a line around, encircle; to confine within limits, restrict
After major surgery, patients may need to ____________________ their physical activities for a while.

UNIT 7

*Read the following passage, taking note of the **boldface** words and their contexts. These words are among those you will be studying in Unit 7. It may help you to complete the exercises in this Unit if you refer to the way the words are used below.*

Everything That Happens, Happens as It Should

<First-Person Narrative>

What a day! I am shivering and my feet are swollen from our long, grueling march, yet I must first attend to the needs of my master, Emperor Marcus Aurelius. We are on the northern frontier, on a campaign to put down an uprising of a rogue Germanic tribe. These barbarians fired the first **salvo** yesterday, raining arrows down on a number of our brave legionnaires. Today we moved to higher ground to gain **momentum** for an attack.

My master is exhausted and takes his dinner alone this evening, without his generals. I am starving but would not **presume** to eat. At least I got to taste a little beef and wine, as I sample everything first in case a foe tries to poison him. I am ever **vigilant** to possible plots against his life, and I trust no one, although I know my master trusts me. As well he should, for I was sold into slavery before birth to pay off my father's debts and have been in the Imperial household all my life.

We have been gone from Rome many months. Life is hard for all of us, from emperor and general to foot soldier and slave. But our monarch is benevolent, and **foremost** a devoted thinker and philosopher. Perhaps that is why he is rarely **flustered**, even when facing misfortune and suffering. For if Marcus is not putting down uprisings from uncouth savages, he is placating unruly senators prone to fighting and **brawling**. To me, these men display a **flagrant** disregard for the respect due an emperor. It's appalling!

The Stoic philosophy Marcus Aurelius subscribes to declares that all men are, by nature, equal. "Blasius," he said to me the other day, "you are cold. Go to the provisions tent and get warmer clothes." My master has **nurtured** my education, and so I have grown **proficient** in reading, writing, and music. Sometimes I play the lute while he converses with me. I pretend we are friends and equals instead of master and slave. I long for our days at the Imperial palace or at one of the country villas, with the many luxuries. Oh, what I would give for the taste of a honey-drenched fig! I also miss my dear friend, Grumio; I rarely see him even in Rome, for he is a **domestic** slave in the house of a rich merchant on the other side of the city.

Still, questioning my lot in life will get me nowhere. Marcus **detests** complaining and has told me many times that things are as they are and as they are meant to be, so I won't incur his **wrath** by appearing ungrateful. My friend Gaius, a freed slave, chose to fight as a gladiator for fame and fortune. Gaius is still alive, but just barely. Whereas I live a charmed life in comparison, thanks to my master.

Marcus Aurelius often reminds me that no man is given more hardship than he can endure. Even out here, in the midst of battle, he writes daily of life's **paradoxes** and how to accept the idea that what looks like contradiction may be true. He says he is **flawed**, like all men, but he has had a long reign over an unruly empire and is strong and unbowed. As for me, I wish that I had one-quarter of his fortitude and courage!

Audio

For iWords and audio passages, go to **SadlierConnect.com**.

Definitions

Note the spelling, pronunciation, part(s) of speech, and definition(s) of each of the following words. Then write the appropriate form of the word in the blank space in the illustrative sentence(s) following.

1. brawl (brôl)
(*n.*) a noisy quarrel or fight; (*v.*) to quarrel or fight noisily
The noise coming from the classroom sounded more like a ____________________ than a debate.

2. detest (di test′)
(*v.*) to hate, dislike very much, loathe
Children who dislike green vegetables often ____________________ spinach.

3. flagrant (flā′ grənt)
(*adj.*) extremely bad, glaring; scandalous, notorious
Crossing against the light shows a ____________________ disregard for the law.

4. fluster (fləs′ tər)
(*v.*) to make or become confused, agitated, or nervous; (*n.*) a state of confusion or agitation
During the trial, the judge told the attorney not to ____________________ the witness.

5. momentum (mō ment′ əm)
(*n.*) the force or speed with which something moves
The presidential campaign gained ____________________ once the first primary was over.

6. notable (nōt′ ə bəl)
(*adj.*) striking, remarkable; (*n.*) a person who is well known, distinguished, or outstanding in some way
Being chosen for the team was a ____________________ event in our lives.
The party was attended by ____________________ from the film world.

7. paradox (par′ ə däks)
(*n.*) a self-contradictory statement that on closer examination proves true; a person or thing with seemingly contradictory qualities
It is a ____________________ to say that youth is wasted on the young.

8. prior (prī′ ər)
(*adj.*) earlier, former
Unfortunately, the governor had a ____________________ appointment and could not meet with the class.

9. salvo
(sal′ vō)

(*n.*) a burst of gunfire or cannon shot, often as a tribute or salute; a sudden burst of anything; a spirited verbal attack

The audience erupted in a ____________________ of laughter.

10. vigilant
(vij′ ə lənt)

(*adj.*) wide-awake, alert, watchful

The ____________________ guards paced back and forth in front of the barracks.

Using Context

For each item, determine whether the ***boldface*** *word from pages 102–103 makes sense in the context of the sentence. Circle the item numbers next to the six sentences in which the words are used correctly.*

1. The statement "I know one thing, and that is that I know nothing" is a famous **paradox** attributed to the ancient Greek philosopher Socrates.

2. In 1920, the 19th Amendment to the U.S. Constitution took effect, and American women were finally able to **detest** their right to vote.

3. The police officers were especially **vigilant** because a series of robberies had recently occurred in the neighboring town.

4. Everyone was shocked by the **flagrant** disrespect that the player showed for the referee.

5. We must not let minor setbacks **fluster** us or spoil our determination to successfully complete the project.

6. Every year, a few of the world's most **notable** musicians are inducted into the Rock & Roll Hall of Fame.

7. It will take days to clean out the **brawl** that was left in the basement after the muddy floodwaters receded.

8. At the beginning of each lesson on a topic such as butterflies or magnets, the science teacher encouraged students to share their **prior** knowledge.

9. In most places on Earth, the seasons change as the planet makes its yearly **momentum** around the sun.

10. After the hiker was bitten by a snake, he was quickly airlifted to a hospital so that doctors could treat him with a **salvo** for the venom.

Choosing the Right Word

*Select the **boldface** word that better completes each sentence. You might refer to the passage on pages 100–101 to see how most of these words are used in context. Note that the choices might be related forms of the Unit words.*

1. *Romeo and Juliet* opens with members of the rival houses of Montague and Capulet (**brawling, flustering**) in the streets of Verona.
2. It was hard to believe that the small, rather ordinary-looking person who was standing before us was a world-famous (**notable, salvo**).
3. I am disturbed by the (**momentum, paradox**) of impoverished people in the richest land on Earth.
4. The struggle against terrorism has been one of the (**notable, flagrant**) features of our time.
5. As support for our candidate continued to gain (**momentum, salvo**), it soon became clear that she would win the election by a landslide.
6. I can forgive an honest mistake, but I (**brawl, detest**) any attempt to cover up errors by lying.
7. The unexpected award left me in a confused but thrilling (**fluster, momentum**).
8. The charges of incompetence the candidate leveled at her opponent were but the opening (**brawl, salvo**) in her campaign to become mayor.
9. Though I hadn't expected to be treated quite so unkindly by the audience, I didn't become (**flustered, detested**) or lose my professional cool.
10. No parent can ever be (**vigilant, flagrant**) enough to prevent a small child from taking many a painful tumble.
11. Because there had been no (**prior, vigilant**) notice of the scholarship competition, we had practically no time to prepare for it.
12. How can you expect the court to excuse your repeated and (**flagrant, vigilant**) violations of the traffic laws?

Completing the Sentence

Choose the word from the word bank that best completes each of the following sentences. Write the correct word or form of the word in the space provided.

brawl	flagrant	momentum	paradox	salvo
detest	fluster	notable	prior	vigilant

1. I wouldn't call such a(n) ____________________ and premeditated lie merely a "minor lapse of memory."

2. Some people truly love the music of such modern composers as Arnold Schoenberg or Igor Stravinsky; others absolutely ____________________ it.

3. In the old days, wooden battleships saluted their victorious admiral by repeatedly firing ____________________ of cannon shot from their decks.

4. At what point does a spinning top lose sufficient ____________________ to topple over?

5. The speaker went right on with his speech, in no way ____________________ or disturbed by the jeers and catcalls of a few rowdy hecklers.

6. We must be ____________________ in recognizing the early signs of decay in our community and move quickly to improve conditions.

7. That terrible instruments of war should in fact prove useful as guardians of the peace is one of the ____________________ of modern life.

8. It's a fact that some important battles of the American Revolution occurred ____________________ to the signing of the Declaration of Independence.

9. When two players suddenly started to throw punches at each other during last night's game, an ugly bench-clearing ____________________ ensued.

10. Though his career as a whole was not particularly distinguished, he did score one ____________________ success on Broadway a few years ago.

End Set A

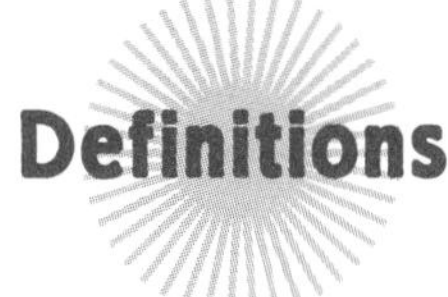

Definitions

Note the spelling, pronunciation, part(s) of speech, and definition(s) of each of the following words. Then write the appropriate form of the word in the blank space in the illustrative sentence(s) following.

1. amiss (ə mis′)
(*adj.*) faulty, imperfect, not as it should be; (*adv.*) in a mistaken or improper way, wrongly

Under the circumstances it would not be ____________________ to offer our congratulations.

2. domestic (də mes′ tik)
(*adj.*) native to a country, not foreign; relating to the life or affairs of a household; (*n.*) a household servant

The newspaper is filled with information about our country's ____________________ affairs.

When my grandmother first came to this country, she took a job as a ____________________.

3. flaw (flô)
(*n.*) a slight fault, defect, crack

We noticed a ____________________ in the plan to start building the house before the spring rains.

4. fledgling (flej′ liŋ)
(*n.*) an inexperienced person, beginner; a young bird about to leave the nest; (*adj.*) inexperienced, budding

We placed the ____________________ back in its nest.

A ____________________ police officer appeared on the scene and wisely called for assistance.

5. foremost (fôr′ mōst)
(*adj.*) chief, most important, primary; (*adv.*) in the first place

Among my interests, music is ____________________.

First and ____________________, you must call home to let your family know you'll be late.

6. nurture (nər′ chər)
(*v.*) to bring up, care for, train, nourish; (*n.*) rearing, training, upbringing

It is wonderful to watch chimpanzees ____________________ their young.

The ____________________ they received as children served them well as they grew into adulthood.

7. perjury (pər′ jə rē)
(*n.*) the act of swearing to a lie

The witness was convicted of ____________________ and was sentenced to serve two years in prison.

8. presume (pri züm′) (*v.*) to take for granted, assume or suppose; to dare, take upon oneself, take liberties
The counselors ____________ that the jobs they had last summer will be theirs this summer as well.

9. proficient (prə fish′ ənt) (*adj.*) skilled, expert, or capable in any field or activity
Dad knows his way around the kitchen and is quite a ____________ cook.

10. wrath (rath) (*n.*) intense anger
In Greek and Roman myths, characters fear the ____________ of the gods.

*For each item, determine whether the **boldface** word from pages 106–107 makes sense in the context of the sentence. Circle the item numbers next to the six sentences in which the words are used correctly.*

1. I feel a sense of calm while performing **domestic** chores, such as cooking or cleaning.
2. Her **proficient** personality is fun at parties, but it can be overwhelming in everyday life.
3. The chief police officer assured the family that finding the person who had broken into their home would be his **foremost** priority.
4. When I walked into the room, my friends acted perfectly cheerful, but I felt that something was **amiss** between the two of them.
5. My friends and I were up discussing good times we'd had together until midnight, when we decided to get some sleep and continue our **wrath** in the morning.
6. Fans of the home team tried to **nurture** the opposing team by yelling insults and jeers.
7. The accomplished writer was once a **fledgling** whose work was rejected by two publishers.
8. Although the witness did not want to incriminate a family member, she refused to commit **perjury** and so told the truth.
9. The movie began by showing a **flaw** between the hero and the villain, and the audience realized that they are sworn enemies.
10. "I **presume** you have been studying hard for this exam, as it is worth a third of your final grade," the teacher said to the class.

Set B

Choosing the Right Word

*Select the **boldface** word that better completes each sentence. You might refer to the passage on pages 100–101 to see how most of these words are used in context. Note that the choices might be related forms of the Unit words.*

1. Abraham Lincoln had very little formal schooling, but his mind was (**nurtured, flawed**) by such great literary works as the Bible and the plays of Shakespeare.
2. Under the American system of justice, any person accused of a crime is (**presumed, flawed**) to be innocent until proven guilty.
3. (**Foremost, Flagrant**) among the reasons that so many millions of immigrants have come to the United States is the desire for freedom.
4. The easternmost tip of Cuba was the first populated area in the region to feel the (**paradox, wrath**) of Hurricane Zelda.
5. She may have given wrong information in court, but this was an honest mistake and certainly does not make her guilty of (**perjury, wrath**).
6. She worked so easily and quietly that at first we did not realize how remarkably (**proficient, amiss**) she was in the laboratory.
7. A happy (**domestic, nurture**) life can afford an executive a great deal of relief from the everyday strains of running a large company.
8. To say that the U.S. Constitution is one of the greatest documents of all time does not mean that it is entirely without (**fledglings, flaws**).
9. "Something is (**foremost, amiss**) in this room," said the detective, peering over the back of the sofa, "and I intend to discover what it is."
10. It was an error only a (**flaw, fledgling**), not a more experienced officer, could have committed.
11. Nowadays (**domestics, fledglings**) are seen more often in old books and movies than in real life.
12. The rather skinny boy whom we had noticed only two years before as a (**prior, fledgling**) quarterback was now an all-American!

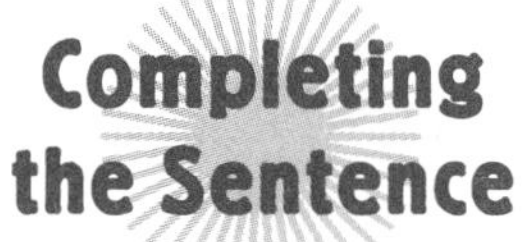

Completing the Sentence

Choose the word from the word bank that best completes each of the following sentences. Write the correct word or form of the word in the space provided.

amiss	flaw	foremost	perjury	proficient
domestic	fledgling	nurture	presume	wrath

1. We suspected that something was ______________________ when he did not return home from school at the usual time.

2. In most respects she is a fine person, but excessive stubbornness is the one important ______________________ in her character.

3. I well remember how often during my childhood I felt the full force of my parents' ______________________ when I had done something wrong.

4. ______________________ among her many outstanding qualities is her ability to understand the points of view of other people.

5. I have no way of knowing for sure why she left, but I ______________________ that she had a good reason for doing so.

6. I must warn you once again that if you fail to tell the truth, you may lay yourself open to a charge of ______________________.

7. The minister saw from the statistics that imported goods were cutting into the ______________________ market.

8. Like a(n) ______________________ eagle about to leave the nest for the first time, our son is preparing to spend his first summer away from home.

9. Her parents ______________________ her musical talents by hiring the finest teachers and taking her to hear the performances of great musicians.

10. How do you explain the fact that some students who do poorly in math are highly ______________________ in figuring out batting averages?

End Set B

*Choose the word or form of the word from this Unit that is the same or most nearly the same in meaning as the **boldface** word or expression in the phrase. Write that word on the line. Use a dictionary if necessary.*

1. did not **rattle** the experienced pilot ______________
2. became an **able** gymnast after much practice ______________
3. felt her enemy's **fury** ______________
4. startled by the **speed** of the jet ______________
5. an **imperfection** in the movie's ending ______________
6. suspected that something had gone **off target** ______________
7. stay **attentive** around the big, hungry dog ______________
8. help to explain the **contradiction** ______________
9. shot a **volley** of arrows ______________
10. the world's **leading** expert on the subject ______________
11. witnessed an unexpected street **scuffle** ______________
12. **surmised** that she passed the test ______________
13. **foster** the child's musical talent ______________
14. a case of **blatant** discrimination ______________
15. was responsible for a variety of **household** chores ______________

*Choose the word or form of the word from this Unit that is most nearly opposite in meaning to the **boldface** word or expression in the phrase. Write that word on the line. Use a dictionary if necessary.*

1. had no **subsequent** arrests ______________
2. a witness's **honesty** on the stand ______________
3. **love** the way he coaches his team ______________
4. an **ordinary** person to speak on our behalf ______________
5. a real **old-timer** at the game of chess ______________

Writing: Words in Action

Relate what you learned about Blasius and his circumstances. Do you agree that everything that happens in Blasius's world has happened as it should? Write an argument stating and defending your opinion. Use at least three details from the passage (pages 100–101) and three or more words from this Unit.

Vocabulary in Context

*Some of the words you have studied in this Unit appear in **boldface** type. Read the passage below, and then circle the letter of the correct answer for each word as it is used in context.*

Marcus Aurelius was the fifth and final Roman ruler in a series often called "the five good emperors." These **notable** sovereigns of ancient Rome ruled from 96 to 180 CE.

Edward Gibbon, the great eighteenth-century historian, called this period the era in which "the condition of the human race was the most happy and prosperous." According to Gibbon, no **prior** or subsequent era could match it. Gibbon was clearly convinced that these five good emperors deserved great credit, and he should not be accused of **perjury** or bias on account of his praise for them.

Why did so little go **amiss** for the Romans in the second century CE? Even a **fledgling** historian would be compelled to admit that the good emperors were sound statesmen and gifted administrators. Their vocation was to benefit their subjects, not to **detest** them.

Among the five good emperors, Trajan usually receives the most attention. It was during his rule, from the years 98 to 117, that the Roman Empire greatly expanded its territory. Trajan's successor, Hadrian, (r. 117–138) was notable for his interest in the welfare of the provinces that Rome ruled. Pius's reign (138–161) was marked by internal peace and prosperity and Marcus Aurelius, of course, was noted for his achievements in philosophy.

Nerva, the first of the five emperors, is often underrated. Chosen by the Senate in 96 CE, he ruled for only two years. Yet his reign is characterized by relief programs for the poor and an interest in public education. Most importantly, under his rule, Nerva began the practice of adopting imperial successors—a policy that saved Rome from much political infighting for nearly a century.

---

1. What is the meaning of **notable** as it is used in paragraph 1?

a. casual
b. remarkable
c. tyrannical
d. questionable

2. What is the meaning of **prior** as it is used in paragraph 2?

a. lesser
b. briefer
c. longer
d. former

3. What does the word **perjury** most likely mean as it is used in paragraph 2?

a. false logic
b. favoritism
c. false witness
d. near-sightedness

4. The word **amiss** means about the same as

a. wrongly
b. well
c. plainly
d. justly

5. Which word means the same as **fledgling** as it is used in paragraph 3?

a. biased
b. specialized
c. acclaimed
d. inexperienced

6. **Detest** comes from the Latin word **detestari. Detestari** most likely means

a. to praise
b. to curse
c. to defer
d. to cancel

UNIT 8

*Read the following passage, taking note of the **boldface** words and their contexts. These words are among those you will be studying in Unit 8. It may help you to complete the exercises in this Unit if you refer to the way the words are used below.*

A Fish That Fishes

<Magazine Article>

by Laverne J. Cambalda, Ph.D.

A fish that fishes? Can such a creature really exist in the natural order of things? One might at first be inclined to deny the possibility, but at the risk of being **disputatious**, the answer is yes. The creature that appears to use rod and lure to capture its prey is known as the anglerfish. One glance at this bizarre denizen of the deep suffices to establish its appearance as **abnormal** in the extreme.

The old adage points out that "it takes one to know one." But human observers of this creature do not even need to be anglers themselves to recognize the uncanny resemblance of the anglerfish's projecting spine to a fishing rod.

By the same token, the fleshy **nub** at the end of the spine, called the esca, resembles a lure. Even more strangely, the esca sometimes appears lit up in the murky ocean depths due to a phenomenon known as bioluminescence—this shining in the dark is, in fact, caused by clusters of bacteria.

Such a setup often spells **catastrophe** for the anglerfish's prey: skatefish, haddock, cod, whiting, and sand eels. An offensive **onslaught** by an anglerfish is formidable. The angler's head is enormous, with a huge mouth ringed with needle-sharp teeth. If a potential victim succumbs to the **incentive** of the lure, the contest is almost always over. The anglerfish comes equipped with a remarkable triggering mechanism; any external contact with its spinelike tentacle will trigger a virtually **simultaneous**, immediate rapid-fire bite. This swiftness almost invariably **outstrips** any defensive actions by the prey.

The cavernous size of the angler's mouth means that it can capture even cautious, **prudent** prey by making even the slightest **swerve** in any direction. Sometimes, moreover, the prey can be twice the angler's own size. Indeed, anglerfish are said to possess the fastest biting action of any vertebrate.

Reassuringly, boaters who **capsize** are unlikely to encounter an anglerfish when they hit the water. Anglers are deep-sea residents, living a mile or more below the surface.

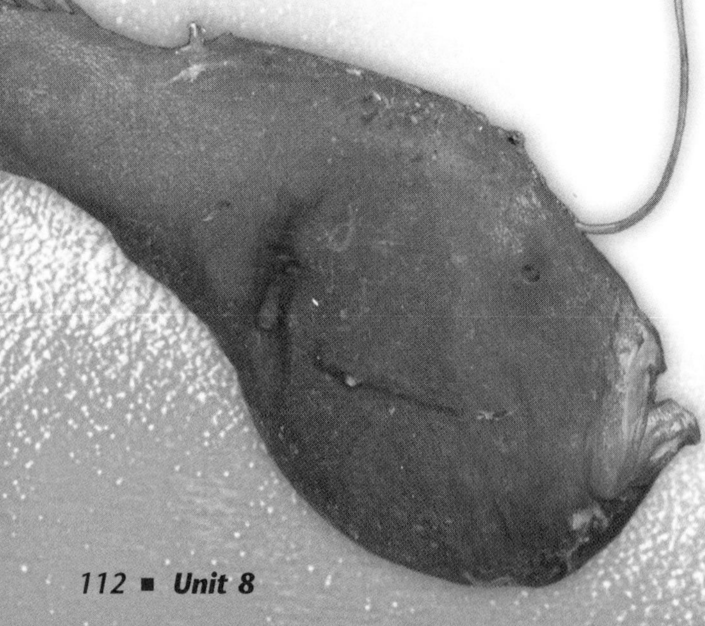

Anglerfish occur worldwide, and they are generally divided into four groups: batfish, frogfish, deep-sea anglerfish, and goosefish. Of the 200 species of anglerfish, some can be tiny, measuring only one-fourth of an inch, while others may stretch up to six feet long. Scientists agree that thanks to their remote habitat and effective "fishing" techniques, anglerfish are **flourishing**. In this respect, as in so many others, they differ from other marine species, many of which are in decline.

Some curious differences separate male anglerfish from females. Only the female angler, for example, comes armed for fishing with the spine and the esca. Males, overall, are much smaller than females. In fact, throughout their lives males actually **decrease** in size. A male attaches itself to a female's body, becoming completely dependent on her. One can only imagine the consequences of any **insubordination** on his part!

Ultimately, the male's body dwindles to a mere **remnant**. He has become merely a fertilizing mechanism for the female.

Such is the remarkable world of the anglerfish—both intriguing and demanding but perfectly suited for the anglerfish.

Laverne J. Cambalda, Ph.D., has been fascinated by marine life since she first saw the ocean. A native of Nebraska, Cambalda moved to Monterey, California, after she went to graduate school to study marine biology. This is her first article for Ocean Seven *magazine.*

Audio

For iWords and audio passages, go to **SadlierConnect.com**.

Definitions

Note the spelling, pronunciation, part(s) of speech, and definition(s) of each of the following words. Then write the appropriate form of the word in the blank space in the illustrative sentence(s) following.

1. abnormal
(ab nôr′ məl)

(*adj.*) not usual, not typical, strange

For my sister, who is always late, being early for class would be an ________________ situation.

2. catastrophe
(kə tas′ trə fē)

(*n.*) a large-scale disaster, misfortune, or failure

During the Cold War, the United States did everything possible to avoid a nuclear ________________.

3. decrease
(*v.*, di krēs′; *n.*, dē′ krēs)

(*v.*) to become or make less; (*n.*) a lessening

The manager hopes that theft will ________________ once the new security system is installed.

Because of a sharp ________________ in sales, the company had to lay off two-thirds of its workers.

4. flourish
(flər′ ish)

(*v.*) to grow, thrive, be prosperous; to wave in the air; (*n.*) a dramatic gesture; a fanfare of horns

It is fortunate for lovers of the arts that painting and opera still ________________ in Italy.

Actors often enter the stage with a ________________.

5. insubordinate
(in sə bôrd′ ən ət)

(*adj.*) disobedient, rebellious

The ________________ soldier repeatedly interrupted his commanding officer.

6. onslaught
(än′ slôt)

(*n.*) a violent attack; a sudden rush of something

To prepare for the ________________ of winter, we replenished our supply of firewood and rock salt.

7. outstrip
(aüt strip′)

(*v.*) to get ahead of, do better than, exceed

By offering customers low prices and good terms, the new store hopes to ________________ the competition.

8. prudent
(prüd′ ənt)

(*adj.*) cautious, careful, showing good sense

It pays to make ________________ investments.

9. quench (kwench) — (*v.*) to put out, extinguish, end
The firefighters will ____________________ the flames with water.

10. swerve (swərv) — (*v.*) to turn aside sharply; (*n.*) a sharp or sudden turn
Be aware that if you ____________________ too sharply, you may lose control of the car.
The sudden ____________________ of the bus caused some passengers to fall out of their seats.

Using Context

*For each item, determine whether the **boldface** word from pages 114–115 makes sense in the context of the sentence. Circle the item numbers next to the six sentences in which the words are used correctly.*

1. As soon as I learned that I had been mispronouncing her name all evening, I tried to find her so I could apologize for my **flourish**.
2. According to experts, it is a good idea for all of us—and not just those who are currently experiencing health problems—to **decrease** the amount of sugar and salt in our diets.
3. The wooden stairway that leads down to the beach will have to be rebuilt because it has become **insubordinate**.
4. It may be **abnormal** to have an April snowstorm in New York City, but it is not unheard of.
5. The investigators appeared before the reporters, prepared to answer the **onslaught** of questions that would come up after the plane crash.
6. The team's performance this year is greatly improved; in fact, it has proven to far **outstrip** everyone's expectations.
7. The outdoor theater festival will present a variety of plays, including at least one comedy by Shakespeare and a Greek **catastrophe**.
8. Many of Benjamin Franklin's famous sayings, such as "Three may keep a secret if two of them are dead," seem as **prudent** today as they did more than 200 years ago.
9. The magnificent ship raised its main **swerve** and set out on its long, dangerous voyage.
10. The villain in the story was so ruthless that nothing could **quench** his desire for power.

Choosing the Right Word

*Select the **boldface** word that better completes each sentence. You might refer to the passage on pages 112–113 to see how most of these words are used in context. Note that the choices might be related forms of the Unit words.*

1. After finishing the painting, the artist signed his name in big letters with a playful (**flourish, onslaught**).

2. Has the ability of human beings to produce new inventions (**quenched, outstripped**) our ability to use them wisely?

3. When the musicians failed to arrive and the air-conditioning conked out, we realized that the party was becoming a (**flourish, catastrophe**).

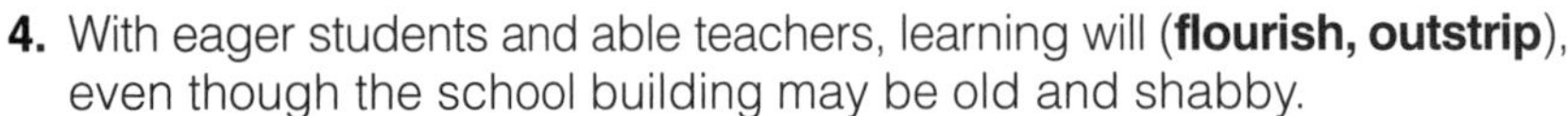

4. With eager students and able teachers, learning will (**flourish, outstrip**), even though the school building may be old and shabby.

5. Even though you may think your supervisor is wrong, you won't be able to hold your job if you act (**prudently, insubordinately**).

6. The high spirits with which we had begun the hike were soon (**outstripped, quenched**) when it began to rain.

7. The only advice I can give you is to take the problems one at a time and deal with each in a sensible and (**prudent, abnormal**) way.

8. There's nothing like pure water to (**quench, flourish**) your thirst.

9. Doesn't it seem (**abnormal, insubordinate**) for a bright young person to show no interest in taking part in any school activities?

10. We have made some progress in cleaning up our community, but that is certainly no reason to (**decrease, swerve**) our efforts.

11. I'm following a very strict study schedule, but I must admit that I (**swerved, flourished**) from it when the play-offs were televised.

12. The first (**onslaught, decrease**) of the disease is marked by a severe fever and the appearance of an ugly rash all over the body.

Choose the word from the word bank that best completes each of the following sentences. Write the correct word or form of the word in the space provided.

abnormal	decrease	insubordinate	outstrip	quench
catastrophe	flourish	onslaught	prudent	swerve

1. The only thing that ever really ____________________ my thirst on a stifling summer afternoon is a glass of ice-cold lemonade.

2. By landing the damaged plane in an open field, the pilot prevented a major ____________________ from occurring.

3. Although we are used to severe winters, a heavy snowfall this early in the season is quite ____________________.

4. When a deer suddenly ran onto the road, the car ____________________ quickly to avoid hitting it.

5. Though we are still the leading producers of various industrial products, other countries are catching up fast and may soon ____________________ us.

6. At the first shock of the enemy's ____________________, our lines wavered a bit, but they soon recovered and held firm.

7. Even the most ____________________ businessperson knows that there are times when it is necessary to take chances.

8. American farms continue to produce more and more food, even though the number of people working on them has actually ____________________.

9. "If that ____________________ young hothead had followed my orders to the letter," the general remarked sourly, "we wouldn't be in this fix!"

10. After our team won the last big game of the season, we all ran out onto the field, ____________________ our pennants and banners jubilantly.

End Set A

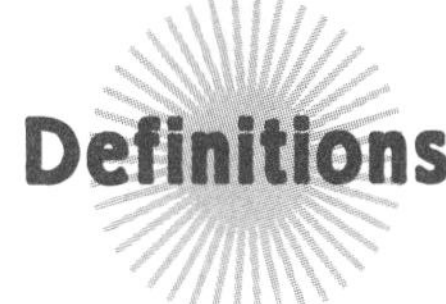

Definitions

Note the spelling, pronunciation, part(s) of speech, and definition(s) of each of the following words. Then write the appropriate form of the word in the blank space in the illustrative sentence(s) following.

1. **capsize** (kap′ sīz) — (*v.*) to turn bottom side up, upset

   Anyone watching could see that it was our inexperience that caused us to ____________________ the canoe.

2. **disputatious** (dis pyü ta′ shəs) — (*adj.*) inclined to argue or debate; provoking debate

   The ____________________ senator had engaged in filibusters to block the passage of many a bill.

3. **evict** (i vikt′) — (*v.*) to force out from a property, eject

   The landlord reluctantly decided to ____________________ the tenants who fell on hard times and had not paid their rent in six months.

4. **incentive** (in sen′ tiv) — (*n.*) a reason for doing something; something that stimulates action

   Because career advancement is such a strong ____________________, adults are usually eager and hard-working students.

5. **legible** (lej′ ə bəl) — (*adj.*) easily read

   In keeping with the jokes, pharmacists will tell you that most doctors' handwriting is barely ____________________.

6. **nub** (nəb) — (*n.*) the central point or heart of a matter; a knob

   After seemingly endless digressions, the speaker finally got to the ____________________ of his argument.

7. **ordain** (ôr dān′) — (*v.*) to establish by law; to order or command; to appoint as a priest or minister; to destine

   Ancient astrologers believed that the stars could ____________________ one's future.

8. **pervade** (pər vād′) — (*v.*) to spread throughout

   Pollutants ____________________ the atmosphere of many of our nation's large cities.

9. remnant (rem′ nənt)
(*n.*) a small part remaining behind
By the end of the war, the rebels had but a ____________ of their former strength.

10. simultaneous (si məl tā′ nē əs)
(*adj.*) happening or existing at the same time
The diplomats put on headphones so that they could listen to a ____________ translation of the speech.

Using Context

*For each item, determine whether the **boldface** word from pages 118–119 makes sense in the context of the sentence. Circle the item numbers next to the six sentences in which the words are used correctly.*

1. As **incentive**, the teacher promised to give a gold star to students who earned the top grades in the class.
2. I thought it was unfair of my parents to **ordain** me from watching television until I brought my grades up, but it actually did encourage me to study more.
3. I tried to **capsize** my friend from auditioning for the play for fear he would embarrass himself, but he turned out to be quite talented.
4. The old letters that my grandparents wrote to each other are barely **legible** after sitting in storage for years.
5. The **nub** of the skyscraper is so high up I had to tilt my head back to see it properly.
6. The two top salespeople in the company made **simultaneous** decisions to quit their jobs, leaving the department at a loss for how to move forward.
7. Although the rumor was nothing more than silly gossip, it continued to **pervade** the school until everyone had heard some version of it.
8. Since my lease states that having a pet is grounds to **evict** me, I am not able to take in my friend's cat while she's away.
9. I feared that I would not be left with a **remnant** of dignity after facing the experienced chess player, but I ended up beating him easily.
10. Your **disputatious** reasoning on your stance is well thought out enough to make me reconsider my opinion.

Set B

Choosing the Right Word

*Select the **boldface** word that better completes each sentence. You might refer to the passage on pages 112–113 to see how most of these words are used in context. Note that the choices might be related forms of the Unit words.*

1. As (**ordained, capsized**) in the U.S. Constitution, the President must be a native-born American at least 35 years old when he or she takes office.

2. "We have become so engrossed in the minor details of the situation that we have left no time to consider the (**nub, incentive**) of the matter," I said.

3. Two of the more (**legible, disputatious**) members of the committee soon got into an argument about where to build the new facility.

4. As we returned to the dressing room after that terrible first half, the whole atmosphere seemed to be (**pervaded, capsized**) by defeat.

5. The possibility of getting a summer job in an office is all the (**incentive, remnant**) I need to improve my computer skills.

6. Months after the fire, a strong scent of charred wood (**pervaded, ordained**) the forest.

7. All our hopes and plans were (**capsized, ordained**) when we learned that we would not be able to attend the music festival.

8. When the elderly pianist began to play, we were saddened to observe that he had only a(n) (**incentive, remnant**) of his once great skill.

9. After the protesters had been sleeping in the building for two months, the police finally (**evicted, ordained**) them.

10. To get a good grade, make sure that your composition is interesting in content, correct in grammar and spelling, and (**simultaneous, legible**).

11. The train and the car approached the crossing almost (**simultaneously, disputatiously**), and a terrible accident seemed unavoidable.

12. It seemed that fate had (**capsized, ordained**) that I was not to get to the job interview, as my bus broke down on the way.

Completing the Sentence

Choose the word from the word bank that best completes each of the following sentences. Write the correct word or form of the word in the space provided.

capsize	evict	legible	ordain	remnant
disputatious	incentive	nub	pervade	simultaneous

1. As the holidays approached, a feeling of excitement and anticipation seemed to ____________________ the entire school.

2. When that land is developed into a mall, the city will ____________________ any illegal squatters and offer them other alternatives for living situations.

3. My brother was ____________________ a priest after he had completed his studies at the seminary.

4. The writing on the curious old document had faded badly, but it was still perfectly ____________________ when held up to the light.

5. Trying to avoid an argument with that ____________________ fellow is like trying to nail oatmeal to the wall.

6. After I had eaten my fill, I threw the ____________________ of my dinner into the dog's bowl.

7. Do you really believe that making money is the only ____________________ that leads people to work hard and try to excel?

8. When my canoe unexpectedly hit a tree stump and ____________________, I suddenly found myself neck-deep in some very cold and dirty water.

9. The secret of the trick is to remove the first card and pick up the second so quickly that the two actions seem to be ____________________.

10. Let's ignore minor side issues and get to the ____________________ of the problem as quickly as possible.

End Set B

Synonyms

*Choose the word or form of the word from this Unit that is the same or most nearly the same in meaning as the **boldface** word or expression in the phrase. Write that word on the line. Use a dictionary if necessary.*

1. tried to **slake** her thirst with water ______________
2. clothing **saturated** with the liquid ______________
3. winds that could **overturn** the boat ______________
4. scolded for being **unruly** ______________
5. was a mediator between the **quarrelsome** neighbors ______________
6. was forced to **veer** to the right ______________
7. left with only a **fragment** of her pride ______________
8. **surpass** sales from last year ______________
9. pain that **lessened** with time ______________
10. unable to attend two **concurrent** shows ______________
11. witnessed the **calamity** of war ______________
12. fell over from the wave's **assault** ______________
13. will offer a free trip as an **inducement** ______________
14. finally got to the **core** of the matter ______________
15. **appointed** a minister ______________

Antonyms

*Choose the word or form of the word from this Unit that is most nearly opposite in meaning to the **boldface** word or expression in the phrase. Write that word on the line. Use a dictionary if necessary.*

1. a note in **messy** handwriting ______________
2. will not **take in** any tenants ______________
3. a **diminishing** fox population ______________
4. made an **unwise** decision ______________
5. exhibited **typical** behavior ______________

Writing: Words in Action

Write a summary of the article about the anglerfish (pages 112–113). Your summary should be no more than half the length of Dr. Cambalda's original text and should use your own words. Include all the key facts in the article, and omit minor details. Use three or more words from this Unit.

Vocabulary in Context

*Some of the words you have studied in this Unit appear in **boldface** type. Read the passage below, and then circle the letter of the correct answer for each word as it is used in context.*

If you need help twisting a stubborn jar lid, you might want to ask a giant Pacific octopus. In laboratory experiments, these intriguing creatures have learned to open jars. Sure, having eight arms probably helps, but they've also figured out how to solve mazes and play with toys. When it comes to smarts, the intelligent invertebrates **outstrip** their fellow ocean dwellers.

The giant Pacific octopus is the largest species of octopus in the world. They average about 16 feet in length and 110 pounds in weight, although those in aquariums tend to be smaller. These octopuses are usually reddish-pink; it is not possible to **ordain** their color. They use a sophisticated camouflage system to control the color, pattern, and even texture of their skin to hide from predators. If discovered, octopuses will release a cloud of black ink to confuse their attackers. The octopus's eight arms are studded with powerful suction cups for gripping prey. Each arm is controlled separately, by a set of neurons at the base. The long, graceful appendages gather food and **evict** enemies.

Giant Pacific octopuses like to be alone, except to mate. They live in shallow, coastal Pacific waters from Korea and Japan north to Alaska and south to Southern California. They can often be found in tide pools. Pollutants **pervade** the oceans and threaten all marine life, including octopuses. Scientists and environmentalists are taking steps to help **quench** the threat. Giant Pacific octopuses may be brainy, but don't ask one to send you a postcard. They have eight arms, but that's no guarantee their writing will be **legible**!

---

1. What is the meaning of **outstrip** as it is used in paragraph 1?

a. outperform **c.** lose to
b. amuse **d.** frighten

2. Which word means the same as **ordain** as it is used in paragraph 2?

a. maintain **c.** reproduce
b. destined **d.** translate

3. **Evict** comes from the Latin word **evincere**. **Evincere** most likely means

a. to defeat **c.** to trap
b. to eat **d.** to frighten

4. In paragraph 3, what does the word **pervade** suggest about pollutants?

a. They touch. **c.** They protect.
b. They permeate. **d.** They decay.

5. The word **quench** means about the same as

a. end **c.** criticize
b. accept **d.** increase

6. What does **legible** most likely mean as it is used in paragraph 3?

a. quickly resolved **c.** easily read
b. strictly observed **d.** hurriedly undertaken

UNIT 9

*Read the following passage, taking note of the **boldface** words and their contexts. These words are among those you will be studying in Unit 9. It may help you to complete the exercises in this Unit if you refer to the way the words are used below.*

Marc Chagall

<Biographical Sketch>

Marc Chagall (1887–1985) was one of the most celebrated and prolific artists of the twentieth century. He was born Moishe Shagal, eldest of nine children, to an oppressed and **downtrodden** but proud Orthodox Jewish family in Vitebsk, a port city in Russia. His father, Khatskel, labored in a herring factory. His mother, Feiga-Ita, ran a small grocery shop.

Shagal exhibited impressive artistic talent early on. But money was tight, and his father tried to **stifle** his son's ambition. Why couldn't his son devote himself fully to his faith and family? And how could he support himself on an artist's **puny** income?

Chagall in front of his stained-glass window at the United Nations, 1964

But Shagal had far-reaching dreams. He was not going to be a humble **bystander** in the world. He believed he saw things that "regular" people did not see. He represented people, animals, flowers, religious symbols, and his own dreams in **vital**, lively paintings. People flew in the sky, and size and scale were often ignored.

Shagal **persisted** with his dreams, and in 1907, with his mother's help, he went to St. Petersburg, then the capital of Russia and a cultural center, to study art. While he learned valuable skills and techniques, he **floundered** and struggled for a time. Many of his days in the cosmopolitan city were an **ordeal**. He had to roll up his sleeves and work as a servant to pay bills, and he was jailed once for not having working papers.

Poverty and struggle followed him, but his confidence in his talent never **eroded**. Shagal moved to Paris in 1910, changing his name to the more French-sounding Marc Chagall. He enrolled in an art academy. He befriended other artists and spent hours studying those he admired.

It was in Paris that his vivid, **graphic** images took shape, and his distinctive way of depicting his worldview **accelerated**. He said, "My art needed Paris like a tree needs water." Chagall invented his own style. In spite of his **melancholy** childhood and tough times, his family, his early village life, his faith and belief in tradition were mainstays of his enchanting paintings. Chagall

"Birthday" ("L'Anniversaire"), 1915. Digital Image © The Museum of Modern Art/Licensed by SCALA/Art Resource, NY.

stayed close to his humble origins, for one sees great things from the valley and only small things from the peak.

In 1914, Chagall returned to Vitebsk, **enticed** by his fiancée, Bella Rosenfeld, a **regal**, cultured woman and his muse. He stayed in Russia after the outbreak of World War I and during the 1917 Russian Revolution. He and Bella eventually returned to Paris in 1923, and Chagall became a French citizen. Then World War II broke out in 1939, and he was swept up in the **gruesome** horror of war, the persecution of the Jews, revolutions, and personal tragedy. Chagall fled to the United States in 1941. He and his family took whatever paintings they could save as he went into exile. Chagall spent seven happy and productive years in the United States. He then returned to France for the remainder of his life.

During Chagall's long career, he experimented with many different art forms, from painting to tapestries to theatrical set designs to stained glass. His stained-glass commissions include a series of Biblical windows for a synagogue in Jerusalem. He also created the famous "Peace" window at the United Nations building in New York. The lobby of the Metropolitan Opera House at Lincoln Center, in midtown Manhattan, is the venue for one of his most beloved works, immense murals called "The Triumph of Music" and "The Sources of Music."

Audio

For iWords and audio passages, go to **SadlierConnect.com.**

Definitions

Note the spelling, pronunciation, part(s) of speech, and definition(s) of each of the following words. Then write the appropriate form of the word in the blank space in the illustrative sentence(s) following.

1. bystander (bī′ stan dər)
(*n.*) one who looks on or observes, a person present but not taking part
The ________________ who had witnessed the collision gave his statement to the police.

2. canvass (kan′ vəs)
(*v.*) to go through an area in order to procure votes, sales, or opinions; to go over in detail; to discuss
The students volunteered to ________________ the neighborhood for our candidate.

3. downtrodden (daůn′ träd ən)
(*adj.*) treated unfairly and cruelly, oppressed
Most of the immigrants at Ellis Island represented the ________________ masses yearning to be free.

4. erode (i rōd′)
(*v.*) to wear away gradually, eat away
Storms and mudslides ________________ the road so that eventually it became impassable.

5. gruesome (grü′ səm)
(*adj.*) horrible, revolting, ghastly
The ________________ crime rocked the ordinarily quiet neighborhood.

6. melancholy (mel′ ən käl ē)
(*adj.*) sad, gloomy, unhappy; (*n.*) sadness, gloominess
It must have been the gloom of the house and the steady rain that made me feel so ________________.
The tune and the lyrics of the song were filled with ________________.

7. ordeal (ôr dēl′)
(*n.*) a difficult or painful experience, a trial
The climbers were exhausted by their ________________ and quickly fell asleep.

8. persist (pər sist′)
(*v.*) to continue steadily in a course of action, refuse to stop or be changed; to last, remain
Despite stern warnings from their doctor, the brothers ________________ in their bad habits.

9. quibble (kwib′ əl)
(*v.*) to evade or belittle a point by twisting words or raising minor objections; (*n.*) a petty objection

Let's not ____________ over details.

The buyer's ____________ notwithstanding, the parties soon came to an agreement.

10. vital (vīt′ əl)
(*adj.*) having life, living; necessary to life, essential; key, crucial

The treaty is of ____________ importance to the security of our nation.

Using Context

*For each item, determine whether the **boldface** word from pages 126–127 makes sense in the context of the sentence. Circle the item numbers next to the six sentences in which the words are used correctly.*

1. Do you know the answer to the **quibble** "What goes up and down without moving?"
2. In the famous fairy tale, Cinderella starts out as a **downtrodden** and overworked member of her stepmother's household.
3. Before you send out that email, be sure to reread it and **erode** any errors in spelling or punctuation that you find.
4. Local officials advised residents to **canvass** three days worth of food and water because of the huge snowstorm that had been predicted.
5. Both the book and the movie *Jaws* begin with a **gruesome** shark attack.
6. The lawyer claimed that his client had not participated in the fight; rather, he was just an innocent **bystander**.
7. As the plane took off, the flight attendants presented **vital** safety information to the passengers.
8. The house was filled with the rich, **melancholy** smell of freshly baked biscuits.
9. After being rescued, the miners described their 10-day **ordeal** and sincerely thanked those who had saved them.
10. If our dog's lack of appetite and seeming tiredness **persist** for two or three more days, we will take her to the veterinarian.

Choosing the Right Word

*Select the **boldface** word that better completes each sentence. You might refer to the passage on pages 124–125 to see how most of these words are used in context. Note that the choices might be related forms of the Unit words.*

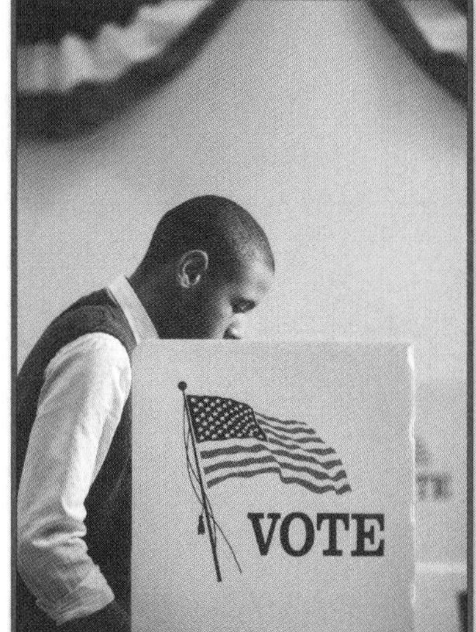

1. In a democracy, the average citizen should be an active participant in public affairs, not just a quiet (**bystander, ordeal**).
2. In spite of the bright sunshine and the happy crowds, a strange mood of (**ordeal, melancholy**) seemed to take possession of me.
3. The assistant principal (**canvassed, quibbled**) the faculty for ways of improving the educational standards of the school.
4. When I asked you what you meant by those words, I wasn't (**quibbling, eroding**) but trying to discover what the problem was.
5. I think it showed bad judgment on your part to tell such a (**gruesome, downtrodden**) story to a child who is so easily frightened.
6. "This case is much more than a mere (**canvass, quibble**) between former friends," said the lawyer during the closing remarks.
7. Sunset on a cold autumn day can be a wistful, (**melancholy, vital**) sight.
8. In spite of all the setbacks we have had, we must (**persist, quibble**) in our efforts to achieve the goal we have set for ourselves.
9. No doubt he has our best interests at heart, but my faith in him has been (**eroded, downtrodden**) by repeated evidence of his poor judgment.
10. If you have prepared properly for the exams, there will be no reason to regard them as a terrible (**quibble, ordeal**).
11. She made what proved to be a (**vital, melancholy**) mistake when she gave the job to one of the applicants without checking his references first.
12. "How can you compare a union employee," the factory owner asked, "to the (**downtrodden, melancholy**) serfs and slaves of earlier times?"

Completing the Sentence

Choose the word from the word bank that best completes each of the following sentences. Write the correct word or form of the word in the space provided.

bystander	**downtrodden**	**gruesome**	**ordeal**	**quibble**
canvass	**erode**	**melancholy**	**persist**	**vital**

1. Although these workers were __________________ in their native land, in the United States they are entitled to a fair wage and safe working conditions.

2. How can he __________________ in denying that he was at the scene of the crime when several people saw him there?

3. Regular visits to the dentist are __________________ if you wish to have healthy, good-looking teeth.

4. A group of reporters from the local TV station __________________ our district for reactions to the proposed changes in the law.

5. Some poets write best about happy events, while others seem to prefer the more __________________ side of life.

6. In our environment class, we learned that in much of the United States, the topsoil has been badly __________________ by natural forces.

7. He now claims that he was just an innocent __________________, but I saw him actually taking part in the fight.

8. The __________________ sight that greeted my eyes at the scene of that awful traffic accident gave me nightmares for weeks.

9. At that tender age, I was so shy that I found it a(n) __________________ to be introduced to people I'd never met before.

10. If you were spending your own money, rather than mine, you would be more inclined to __________________ over the price of the repairs.

End Set A

Definitions

Note the spelling, pronunciation, part(s) of speech, and definition(s) of each of the following words. Then write the appropriate form of the word in the blank space in the illustrative sentence(s) following.

1. accelerate (ak sel′ ə rāt)
(*v.*) to speed up, cause to move faster; to bring about more quickly
The hikers needed to __________ their pace once it became clear that it would soon rain.

2. casual (kazh′ ə wəl)
(*adj.*) happening by chance or on an irregular basis; showing little concern; informal
A __________ remark made by the mayor was taken out of context and used against him by the press.

3. entice (en tīs′)
(*v.*) to attract, tempt
To __________ shoppers into the store, salespersons were giving away coupons for free gifts.

4. flounder (flau̇n′ dər)
(*v.*) to thrash about in a clumsy or ineffective way
After suffering much damage in the storm, the small craft was left to __________ about helplessly.

5. graphic (graf′ ik)
(*adj.*) lifelike, vivid; relating to the pictorial arts
A witness gave the reporter a __________ account of the destruction caused by the tornado.

6. parch (pärch)
(*v.*) to make dry and thirsty; to shrivel with heat
The fields of Oklahoma were __________ by drought in the 1930s.

7. puny (pyü′ nē)
(*adj.*) of less than normal strength or size; of no importance
The wrestler let out a coarse burst of laughter when his __________ opponent entered the ring.

8. ratify (rat′ ə fī)
(*v.*) to approve, give formal approval to, confirm
The legislatures of three-fourths of the states must __________ an amendment to the Constitution.

9. regal (rē′ gəl) — (*adj.*) royal, kinglike; fit for a king

The two families pooled their resources to give the bride and groom a truly ____________ wedding.

10. stifle (stī′ fəl) — (*v.*) to smother, prevent from breathing; to hold back or choke off

Unable to ____________ her anger, the sculptor lashed out at her harshest critic.

Using Context

*For each item, determine whether the **boldface** word from pages 130–131 makes sense in the context of the sentence. Circle the item numbers next to the six sentences in which the words are used correctly.*

1. Why is it that trying to **stifle** your laughter only makes you want to laugh harder?
2. When she gave me a vacant stare in response to my question, I wondered if she had not heard me or was simply trying to **flounder** for an answer.
3. His **graphic** answer when we asked where he was made us suspect he had something to hide.
4. When the due date for the project was moved up by a week, we were forced to **accelerate** our pace of working.
5. After a day of working on my feet, I felt so **regal** that I feared my legs would give out at any moment.
6. I was told that I was too **puny** to try out for the football team, which only motivated me to spend my summer building up my strength.
7. Many fairy tales tell of witches in disguise trying to **entice** unsuspecting princesses into their captivity.
8. Talking to a crowd for hours on end is enough to **parch** the mouths of even the most seasoned speakers.
9. The host had told me the dress code for the evening was **casual**, so I was shocked to see other guests in gowns and tuxedos.
10. I spent all day trying to **ratify** every corner of the house until it was sparkling clean, only to find out that my guests would not be coming for dinner after all.

Set B

Choosing the Right Word

*Select the **boldface** word that better completes each sentence. You might refer to the passage on pages 124–125 to see how most of these words are used in context. Note that the choices might be related forms of the Unit words.*

1. With her (**regal, graphic**) bearing and imperious manner, Elizabeth I looked every inch the queen she in fact was.
2. You will never do well in school as long as your attitude toward your studies remains (**graphic, casual**) and unconcerned.
3. I find your offer most (**stifling, enticing**), but my better judgment tells me to have nothing to do with it.
4. It is hard to believe that this sturdy, six-foot basketball star was a (**regal, puny**) 100-pounder only a few years ago.
5. Wearing that thick scarf and ski mask, as well as a heavy coat over layers of clothing, he must have felt hot and (**stifled, enticed**) even in the chilly air.
6. In the heat of the desert afternoon, we felt (**parched, regal**) despite drinking from our canteens every few minutes.
7. The soundness of the basic ideas of the U.S. Constitution has been (**ratified, enticed**) by the experience of more than 200 years.
8. Instead of continuing to (**flounder, accelerate**), we must decide on a goal and start to move toward it.
9. After weeks of no rain, the (**parched, graphic**) earth turned to dust that was blown away by the strong winds.
10. Aided by diagrams on the chalkboard, she gave a summary of her plan so clear and (**graphic, regal**) that it won the full support of the audience.
11. If you press the gas pedal just a little, this car will (**stifle, accelerate**) like a racing vehicle.
12. Do her efforts to (**accelerate, flounder**) our departure mean that she is trying to help us, or just get rid of us?

Completing the Sentence

Choose the word from the word bank that best completes each of the following sentences. Write the correct word or form of the word in the space provided.

accelerate	**entice**	**graphic**	**puny**	**regal**
casual	**flounder**	**parch**	**ratify**	**stifle**

1. She gave us a clear, detailed, and ______________ picture of what is likely to happen if we fail to come to grips with the pollution problem.

2. The sled ______________ with alarming speed as it went down the steep slope.

3. After an hour of trudging along the dusty road under the hot sun, we were so ______________ that all we could think of was cold water.

4. Since the twins' birthday party is by no means a formal affair, I feel assured in saying that ______________ clothing is in order.

5. As we fought the forest fire, we were practically ______________ by the extreme heat and heavy smoke.

6. The President's powers in foreign affairs are limited by the fact that any treaty he may negotiate must be ______________ by a two-thirds vote of the Senate.

7. As soon as he learned that he was to play the king in the play, his whole personality took on an almost ______________ air.

8. According to Greek mythology, the Sirens used their remarkable singing voices to ______________ unwary sailors to watery graves.

9. Though the new halfback looked a little ______________ to us, he managed to hold his own against players twice his size and build.

10. When the inexperienced swimmer realized that he was in very deep water, he panicked and began to ______________ about wildly.

End Set B

Synonyms

*Choose the word or form of the word from this Unit that is the same or most nearly the same in meaning as the **boldface** word or expression in the phrase. Write that word on the line. Use a dictionary if necessary.*

1. would **attract** them with homemade treats ______________
2. survived the painful **test** ______________
3. feeling **depressed** from rainy weather ______________
4. rebuild the **distressed** job market ______________
5. **persevered** to finish the race ______________
6. an **indispensable** organ needed to survive ______________
7. swimmers **thrashing about** in the water ______________
8. struck a **stately** pose ______________
9. tried to **suppress** her cough ______________
10. **poll** voters for their opinions ______________
11. pipes **corroded** by acid ______________
12. **hasten** your pace when walking in the dark ______________
13. described the devastation in **realistic** detail ______________
14. standing among the crowd of **spectators** ______________
15. horrified by the **grisly** sight ______________

Antonyms

*Choose the word or form of the word from this Unit that is most nearly opposite in meaning to the **boldface** word or expression in the phrase. Write that word on the line. Use a dictionary if necessary.*

1. dislike playing on a **waterlogged** field ______________
2. gave their full attention to a **serious matter** ______________
3. every **intentional** detail of his design ______________
4. had a **huge** effect on the outcome ______________
5. expected Congress to **repeal** the legislation ______________

Writing: Words in Action

Suppose that you are Marc Chagall and you are writing a memoir. Choose a period that is covered in the passage (pages 124–125) and tell about the experiences and feelings you had at that time. You may invent details, but be sure they are convincing and serious. Use three or more words from this Unit.

*Some of the words you have studied in this Unit appear in **boldface** type. Read the passage below, and then circle the letter of the correct answer for each word as it is used in context.*

The practice of coloring glass for purposes of illumination and decoration dates back to ancient Rome. Romans created **graphic** designs out of very small pieces of colored glass, and set them, like mosaics, in their window frames. The glass allowed light into their houses, but preserved the privacy of the occupants. These designs did something that mosaics could never do: they glowed.

Although the terms *colored glass* and *stained glass* are often used interchangeably in **casual** conversation, colored glass and stained glass are not the same. This is not just a **quibble**. The difference is that in stained glass, the coloring agent is added during manufacture, and not after.

We owe nearly everything we know about the making of stained glass to a twelfth-century monk named Theophilus. In his book, *On Diverse Arts*, Theophilus gives detailed instructions for the manufacture of stained glass and the creation of stained-glass windows. He describes how he took the time to **canvass** the arts of master glassmakers, observing them in their workshops where the heat was so fierce it could **parch**. He explains how intense heat transforms sand and potash into molten glass. He names the powdered metallic oxides that create color: copper for green, lead for yellow, gold for red, and so on. He gives a full account of the intricate, painstaking process that ends in the "inestimable beauty" of a stained-glass window, which he calls "a picture painted with light." Modern glassmakers still use precisely the same techniques. By so doing, they **ratify** the success of the method Theophilus described.

---

1. The word **graphic** means about the same as

a. hand-drawn
b. literal
c. vivid
d. sensational

2. What is the meaning of **casual** as it is used in paragraph 2?

a. informal
b. complicated
c. unpleasant
d. careless

3. The word **quibble** means about the same as

a. friendship
b. disguise
c. squabble
d. question

4. Which word means the same as **canvass** as it is used in paragraph 3?

a. collect
b. examine
c. dismiss
d. question

5. In paragraph 3, what does the use of the word **parch** suggest about the workshops?

a. They were hot.
b. They were crowded.
c. They were old.
d. They were wet.

6. What does the word **ratify** most likely mean as it is used in paragraph 3?

a. understand
b. contradict
c. affirm
d. illustrate

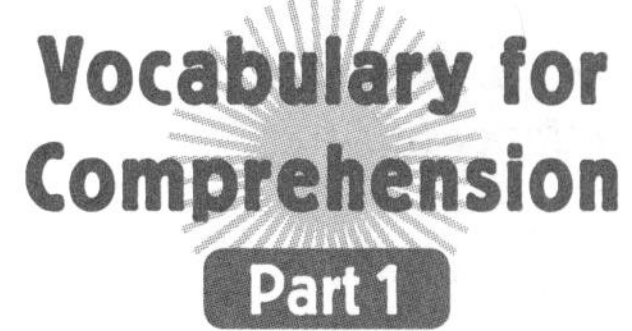

*Read "Agnes Grey," which contains words in **boldface** that appear in Units 7–9. Then answer the questions.*

Agnes Grey

by Anne Brontë

Through our troubles, I never but once heard my mother complain of our want of money, but she observed to Mary and me, "What a desirable thing it would be for your papa to spend a few weeks at a watering-place. I am convinced the sea-air and the change of scene would be of incalculable service to him; but then, you see, there's no money," she added, with a sigh. We both wished exceedingly that the thing might be done. "Well, well!" said she, "it's no use complaining about our ordeal, but something might be done to further the project after all. Mary, you are a beautiful drawer, so what do you say to doing a few more pictures in your best style, and getting them framed, with the drawings you have already done, and trying to dispose of them to some **prudent** picture-dealer, who has the sense to discern their merits?"

"Mamma, I should be delighted if you think they could be sold."

"It's worthwhile trying, however, my dear: do you procure the drawings, and I'll endeavor to find a purchaser."

"I wish I could do something," said I, feeling not a little **downtrodden**.

"You, Agnes! Well, who knows? You draw pretty well, too: if you choose some simple piece for your subject as an **incentive**, I daresay you will be able to produce something we shall all be proud to exhibit."

"But I have **nurtured** another scheme in my head, mamma, and have had long, only I did not like to mention it."

"Indeed! pray tell us what it is."

"I should like to be a governess."

My mother uttered an exclamation of surprise, and my sister dropped her work in astonishment, "You a governess, Agnes! What can you be dreaming of?"

"Well! I don't see what is extraordinary in it. Surely I could teach little ones: and I am so fond of children. Do let me!"

"But, my love, you have not learned to take care of yourself yet: and children require more domestic judgment and experience to manage than elder ones."

"But, mamma," I **persisted,** "I am above eighteen, and quite able to take care of myself, and others too. You do not know half the wisdom and prudence I possess, because I have never been tried."

"Only think," said Mary, "what would you do among strangers, without me or mamma—with a parcel of children, besides yourself, to attend to; and no one to look to for advice? You would not even know what clothes to put on."

"You presume, because I always do as you bid me, I have no judgment of my own: but only try me—that is all I ask—and you shall see what I can do."

At that moment my father entered and the subject of our disputatious discussion was explained to him.

"What, my little Agnes a governess!" cried he, and, in spite of his **melancholy**, he laughed at the idea.

From *Agnes Grey* by Anne Brontë—Public Domain

1. Which inference about the family is supported by details in lines 1–9?
   A) They find their new house less comfortable than they expected.
   B) They find themselves hampered by lack of money.
   C) They have unusual standards for excellence in drawing.
   D) They have failed to agree on how to restore the father's health.

2. **Part A**
   Based on details in the passage, what is the relationship between Mary and the narrator?
   A) They are friends.
   B) They are cousins.
   C) They are sisters.
   D) They are governesses.

   Part B
   Which choice provides the **best** evidence for the answer to the previous question?
   A) "for your papa to spend a few weeks at a watering-place" (lines 5–6)
   B) "the sea-air and the change of scene would be of incalculable service to him" (lines 6–8)
   C) "We both wished exceedingly that the thing might be done" (lines 10–11)
   D) "'but something might be done to further the project after all'"(lines 13–14)

3. What does the word **prudent** most likely mean as it is used in line 19?
   A) successful
   B) frustrated
   C) inexpensive
   D) sensible

4. As it is used in line 28, what does the word **downtrodden** suggest about the narrator?
   A) She feels oppressed.
   B) She is not feeling well.
   C) She wants to be helpful.
   D) She has a positive attitude.

5. What word means the opposite of **incentive** as it is used in line 31?
   A) objection
   B) hindrance
   C) reflection
   D) focus

6. As it is used in line 34, what is the meaning of the word **nurtured**?
   A) raised
   B) rejected
   C) assumed
   D) forgotten

7. As it is used in line 50, what does **persisted** mean?
   A) corrected
   B) complained
   C) continued
   D) pleaded

8. In *Agnes Grey*, why does the mother try to talk Agnes out of her idea to look for a job as a governess?
   A) She thinks Agnes would be better at drawing.
   B) She thinks Mary would be a better governess than Agnes.
   C) She wants Agnes to stay home to take care of her father.
   D) She thinks Agnes has too little experience caring for herself and lacks common sense.

9. Which of the following **best** describes Agnes's reaction to her family's attitude toward her plans?
   A) resigned
   B) spirited
   C) sarcastic
   D) indifferent

10. The word **melancholy** has more than one meaning. As used in line 69, what does the word **melancholy** most likely mean?
    A) depression
    B) outrage
    C) uncertainty
    D) cheerfulness

Vocabulary for Comprehension

Part 2

*Read this passage, which contains words in **boldface** that appear in Units 7–9. Then choose the best answer to each question based on what is stated or implied in the passage. You may refer to the passage as often as necessary.*

Questions 1–10 are based on the following passage.

This passage is adapted from *Great Expectations* by Charles Dickens. Originally published in 1861.

Mr. Pumblechook and I breakfasted at eight o'clock in the parlor behind the shop, while the shopman took his mug of tea and hunch of bread and butter on a sack of peas in the front premises. I **detested** Mr. Pumblechook's wretched company. Besides being possessed by my sister's idea that a mortifying and penitential character ought to be imparted to my diet,—besides giving me as much crumb as possible in combination with as little butter, and putting such a quantity of warm water into my milk that it would have been more candid to have left the milk out altogether,—his conversation consisted of nothing but an **onslaught** of arithmetic. On my politely bidding him Good morning, he said, pompously, "Seven times nine, boy?" And how should *I* be able to answer, dodged in that way, in a strange place, on an empty stomach! Before I had swallowed a **puny** morsel, he began a running sum that **pervaded** breakfast. "Seven?" "And four?" "And eight?" "And six?" "And two?" "And ten?" And so on. And after each figure was disposed of, it was as much as I could do to get a bite before the next came; while he sat at his ease eating bacon and hot roll, in (if I may be allowed the **insubordinate** expression) a gorging and gormandizing manner.

For such reasons, I was very glad when ten o'clock came and we started for Miss Havisham's; though I was not at all at my ease regarding the manner in which I should acquit myself under that lady's roof. Within a quarter of an hour we came to Miss Havisham's house, which was of old brick, and dismal, and had a great many iron bars to it. Some of the windows had been walled up; of those that remained, all the lower were rustily barred. There was a courtyard, and that was barred; so we had to wait, after ringing the bell, until some one would open it.

A window was raised, and a clear, **notable** voice demanded "What name?" To which my conductor replied, "Pumblechook." The voice returned, "Quite right," and the window was shut again, and a young lady came across the courtyard, with keys in her hand.

"This," said Mr. Pumblechook, "is Pip."

"This is Pip, is it?" returned the young lady, who was very pretty and seemed very proud; "come in, Pip."

Mr. Pumblechook was coming in also, when she stopped him with the gate.

"Oh!" she said. "Did you wish to see Miss Havisham?"

"If Miss Havisham wished to see me," returned Mr. Pumblechook, discomfited.

"Ah!" she said; "but you see she don't."

She said it so finally, and in such a **flagrant** way, that Mr. Pumblechook, though in a condition of **eroded** dignity, could not protest. But he eyed me severely,—as if *I* had done anything to him!—and departed with the words reproachfully delivered: "Boy! Let your behavior here be a credit unto them which brought you up!" I was not free from apprehension that he would come back to propound a new **salvo** through the gate, "And sixteen?" But he didn't.

1. According to the first paragraph, Mr. Pumblechook can be described as
   A) kindly and nostalgic.
   B) precise and irritable.
   C) pompous and greedy.
   D) ambitious and secretive.

2. The narrator feels especially bitter about Mr. Pumblechook's
   A) obsession with arithmetic.
   B) fussiness about his own appearance.
   C) social snobbery.
   D) dislike for the narrator's sister.

3. Which choice provides the best evidence for the answer to the previous question?
   A) Lines 1–5 ("Mr. Pumblechook . . . premises")
   B) Lines 5–7 ("I detested . . . company")
   C) Lines 7–16 ("Besides . . . arithmetic")
   D) Lines 26–31 ("And after . . . manner")

4. As it is used in line 22, "puny" most nearly means
   A) undersized.
   B) unappealing.
   C) ripe.
   D) savory.

5. Based on details in paragraph 2 (lines 32–45), Miss Havisham's house might best be described as
   A) stately.
   B) forbidding.
   C) dilapidated.
   D) pretentious.

6. As it is used in line 47, "notable" most nearly means
   A) accented.
   B) loud.
   C) clear.
   D) striking.

7. It can reasonably be inferred that, after his encounter at the entrance to Miss Havisham's house, Mr. Pumblechook feels
   A) relieved.
   B) outraged.
   C) embarrassed.
   D) amused.

8. As it is used in line 65, "flagrant" most nearly means
   A) glaring.
   B) incoherent.
   C) contemptuous.
   D) bemused.

9. As it is used in line 66, "eroded" most nearly means
   A) protracted.
   B) inflated.
   C) abraded.
   D) endangered.

10. The narrator, Pip, concludes this section of the story on a note of
   A) resignation.
   B) humor.
   C) indifference.
   D) criticism.

Synonyms

*From the word bank below, choose the word that has the same or nearly the same meaning as the **boldface** word in each sentence and write it on the line. You will not use all of the words.*

bystander	**foremost**	**onslaught**	**prior**
catastrophe	**graphic**	**ordain**	**ratify**
detest	**legible**	**perjury**	**remnant**
fledgling	**notable**	**presume**	**simultaneous**

1. I couldn't believe my luck when I not only found the ancient document but saw that the writing was actually **decipherable**. ________________

2. We were not prepared for the sudden **assault** of a hailstorm and ran for cover as fast as we could. ________________

3. I decided I could no longer just be an **observer** to the wrongs being committed and was inspired to take action. ________________

4. How can you claim to love going to theme parks when I know that you **despise** large crowds? ________________

5. The **novice** felt overwhelmed her first day on the job and couldn't imagine how she would ever know her way around the office. ________________

6. While not knowing what you'll wear to the dance is an annoyance, I wouldn't exactly call it a **tragedy**. ________________

7. The author's account of the fictional world was so **descriptive** I almost felt like I had visited the place myself. ________________

8. When we reached the top of the mountain, I felt I didn't have even a **residue** of energy left and wondered how I would get back down. ________________

9. I still consider winning the statewide essay contest my most **exceptional** achievement thus far. ________________

10. Although I had no **previous** experience as a volunteer with the organization, I was able to learn quickly. ________________

11. Though the employees do not officially know yet who their new manager will be, they all **surmise** that it is the person who was closest to their old boss. ________________

12. "My **principal** concern is that you take care of yourself and let that leg heal," the doctor told me after my cast was put on. ________________

Select the pair of words that best completes the meaning of each of the following sentences.

1. If you want to stop your automobile, apply the brakes. If you want it to gain ________________, step on the ________________.

a. salvo ... nub
b. momentum ... accelerator
c. incentive ... paradox
d. wrath ... flaw

2. "It isn't ________________ to spend more than you make," I observed. "Only a fool would allow expenses to ________________ income."

a. amiss ... stifle
b. vital ... fluster
c. prudent ... outstrip
d. abnormal ... nurture

3. When prices go up, the value of our money ________________. As the cost of living rises, the more deeply inflation ________________ the purchasing power of the dollar.

a. persists ... perjures
b. flourishes ... parches
c. accelerates ... entices
d. decreases ... erodes

4. "There's nothing ________________ about feeling ________________ after you've been through a disappointment, such as not getting picked for a team," my teacher assured me.

a. abnormal ... melancholy
b. gruesome ... domestic
c. puny ... regal
d. prudent ... casual

5. "An experienced worker doesn't usually have trouble handling a new job with ________________," the personnel manager observed. "A beginner, however, will normally ________________ around until he or she learns the ropes."

a. incentive ... flourish
b. vigilance ... swerve
c. proficiency ... flounder
d. prudence ... quibble

6. My throat became so ________________ during that trek over dusty trails on the hottest day of summer that I firmly believed nothing would ever ________________ my thirst!

a. flagrant ... pervade
b. parched ... quench
c. flawed ... nurture
d. puny ... decrease

7. As we ________________ violently to the right to avoid some rocks that suddenly sprang into view, our canoe ________________ and pitched us headlong into the churning waters of the river.

a. swerved ... capsized
b. brawled ... nurtured
c. flourished ... flustered
d. canvassed ... evicted

WORD STUDY

In the passage about Marc Chagall (see pages 124–125), the author notes that Chagall had to "roll up his sleeves" and work as a servant before he accomplished his dream of becoming an artist.

To "roll up one's sleeves" is an idiom that means to get ready for hard work. An **idiom** is an expression that uses figurative language to express an idea. The meaning of an idiom cannot be guessed from the literal meaning of its words. An idiom must be learned, as if it were a new word or phrase.

Choosing the Right Idiom

*Read each sentence. Use context clues to figure out the meaning of each idiom in **boldface** print. Then write the letter of the definition for the idiom in the sentence.*

1. **Keep an eye on** that snake; don't let it slither away. ______
2. She really **hit the nail on the head** when she said that some people learn best in groups. ______
3. **The ball is in your court** now, so I hope you'll give me an answer soon. ______
4. The sound of those cats wailing in the middle of the night **drives me up the wall**. ______
5. Don't ask me why she did it; **your guess is as good as mine**. ______
6. Please tell us more about the **wild and woolly** days of the Old West. ______
7. **Lend me your ear**, and I'll tell you a tale. ______
8. You complain so much; must you always have **an ax to grind**? ______
9. **Keep your eyes peeled** for Aunt Nina; she should be waiting for us in Terminal B. ______
10. Because we can never know **what lies in store**, I think we're better off not worrying about the future. ______

a. made the exactly right point

b. a readiness to quarrel or find fault

c. It's your turn; it's time for you to make a decision or make a move.

d. what unforeseen events will occur later

e. watch carefully

f. untamed, uncivilized

g. makes me feel crazy

h. Listen to me.

i. watch for

j. I don't know any more about the subject being discussed than you do.

This Greek root appears in **graphic** (page 130), which literally means "having to do with writing." The word now means "lifelike or vivid," "relating to graphs or diagrams," "representation," or "having to do with the visual arts." Some other words based on the same root are listed below.

autobiography	**biography**	**graphite**	**pictograph**
autograph	**geography**	**graphology**	**seismograph**

From the list of words above, choose the one that corresponds to each of the brief definitions below. Write the word in the blank space in the illustrative sentence below the definition. Use a dictionary if necessary.

1. a picture or symbol used to represent an idea in a system of picture writing; a diagram using pictures to represent data
The Lakota used ____________________ to record important events from their past.

2. an instrument that records the direction, force, and duration of earthquakes and other earth tremors
A(n) ____________________ measures the intensity of an earthquake.

3. to write in one's own handwriting; to write one's signature on or in; a signature
Fans hounded the actor for his ____________________.

4. the story of one's own life written by oneself
Helen Keller's ____________________ is entitled *The Story of My Life.*

5. the study of handwriting
Police investigators often rely on ____________________ to help them unlock clues to a criminal's personality.

6. a soft, black form of carbon
The "lead" in lead pencils is actually ____________________.

7. an account of a person's life written by another person; such writings, collectively
Carl Sandburg wrote a famous ____________________ of Abraham Lincoln.

8. the study of Earth's surface, climate, plants, animals, natural resources, people, and industries; the physical features of a place or region
Maps are important tools in the study of ____________________.

UNIT 10

*Read the following passage, taking note of the **boldface** words and their contexts. These words are among those you will be studying in Unit 10. It may help you to complete the exercises in this Unit if you refer to the way the words are used below.*

The Straight History of Orthodontics

<Historical Nonfiction>

Some people look forward to getting braces on their teeth, thinking they look cool. Other people grow **morbid** at the idea. These unwilling patients avoid visiting the orthodontist until resistance becomes **futile**. But anyone who benefits from the orthodontist's trade today should be thankful for the progress this science has made over the centuries. In bygone days, many a butcher **botched** an attempt to remedy a problem that's now easily cured. The pain that once made dental work **notorious** has been minimized by anesthesia. But it took some time for orthodontics to reach its present state.

Fossil remains of crooked human teeth and **cluttered** mouths date back tens of thousands of years. Greek and Roman texts describing the treatment of irregular teeth by the application of pressure date back as far as the fifth century BCE (Before Common Era). Archaeological evidence indicates even earlier use of orthodontic appliances, including artifacts found in rich, **lavish** burial sites in ancient Italy. Another early attempt at braces may have been discovered on Egyptian mummies with **dilapidated** but recognizable metal bands around their teeth. The metal bands may have anchored elastic strings made of catgut. Thus, from at least 1000 BCE, it was known that teeth move in response to pressure.

Techniques for correcting dental irregularities did not advance much until the eighteenth century. French dentists led the way to building orthodontic practice on scientific foundations from which it has not been **dismantled**. The greatest contribution came from Pierre Fauchard. In 1728, Fauchard published the first general study of dentistry. In it, he described the *bandeau*. It was used to expand the arch and correct crowded

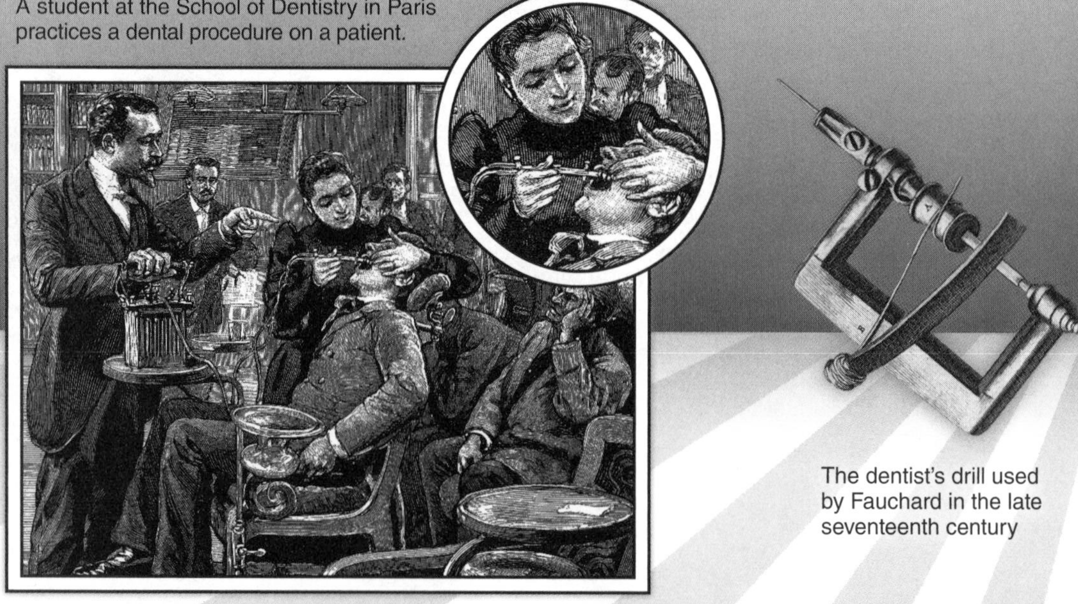

A student at the School of Dentistry in Paris practices a dental procedure on a patient.

The dentist's drill used by Fauchard in the late seventeenth century and crooked teeth. Fauchard described another process of straightening. He filed down a crooked tooth to create **surplus** space around it. Then he repositioned the tooth using a device called a "pelican," a kind of pliers. With the tooth in its proper position, he bound it to its neighbors and let it set. French and English dentists improved on Fauchard's work through the eighteenth century. **Beneficiaries** of Fauchard's treatment may have been grateful when the work was complete. But no doubt many of them faced the prospect of treatment with fearful **timidity** and **bellowed** during the procedures. Indeed, these treatments must have been **grueling** without anesthesia. But evidently there were many Frenchmen who knew that you can't make an omelet without breaking some eggs. Hundreds of patients flocked to Fauchard to **pamper** themselves and improve their looks with dental work.

Pioneering European orthodontists introduced new techniques and instruments in the nineteenth century. Among them were the wire crib, the lever and screw, the chin strap, the use of rubber bands, and plaster models of patients' teeth. By midcentury, the American economy was quite **hospitable** to innovation. American dentists began to take the lead in research and invention. Electricity revolutionized the operating room, and anesthesia made surgery less painful. Norman Kingsley pioneered treatments for cross-bites and cleft palates. John Farrar developed guidelines for using screws to move teeth by applying force in short doses at regular intervals.

The twentieth century saw refinement in the materials and methods of orthodontics. But the fundamental principles of the science were developed during the days of Fauchard. The research performed between then and now has established orthodontics as a profession and opened the way for everyone to benefit from straighter teeth.

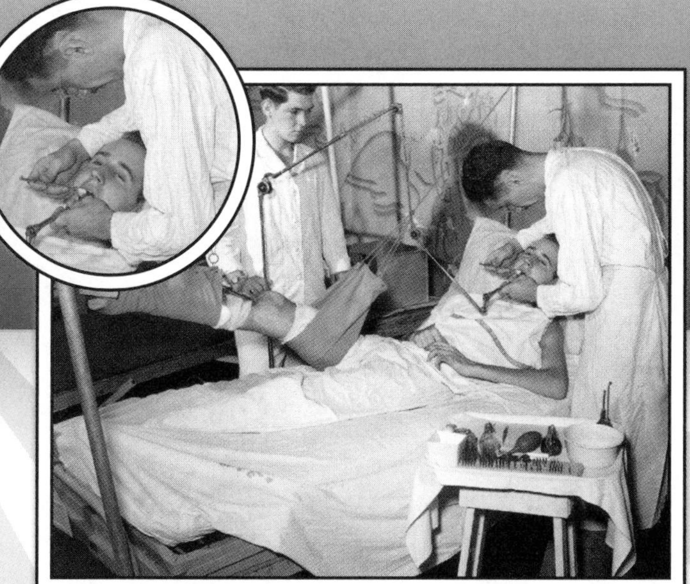

Dental procedures improved a great deal over the twentieth century.

Audio

For iWords and audio passages, go to **SadlierConnect.com**.

Definitions

Note the spelling, pronunciation, part(s) of speech, and definition(s) of each of the following words. Then write the appropriate form of the word in the blank space in the illustrative sentence(s) following.

1. **beneficiary** (ben ə fish′ ē er ē)
   (*n.*) one who benefits from something; a person who is left money or other property in a will or the like
   The ____________________ of the dead man's will was the main suspect in the murder case.

2. **botch** (bäch)
   (*v.*) to repair or patch poorly; make a mess of; (*n.*) a hopelessly bungled job
   The unsupervised laborers proceeded to ____________________ the job badly.

3. **dilapidated** (də lap′ ə dā tid)
   (*adj.*) falling apart or ruined, run-down
   The old house had become so ____________________ that no one could live in it anymore.

4. **futile** (fyüt′ əl)
   (*adj.*) not successful, failing to have any result; useless; unimportant, frivolous
   After several ____________________ attempts to save it, the captain ordered the ship abandoned.

5. **hospitable** (häs pit′ ə bəl)
   (*adj.*) offering friendly or generous treatment to guests; open to anything new or strange
   Known for their generosity to strangers, the local inhabitants offered a ____________________ welcome to our tour group.

6. **lair** (lâr)
   (*n.*) the home or den of a wild animal; any hideout
   The police were making careful preparations to trap the smugglers in their ____________________.

7. **notorious** (nō tôr′ ē əs)
   (*adj.*) widely known because of bad conduct
   Chicago had its share of ____________________ gangsters in the 1930s.

8. **pamper** (pam′ pər)
   (*v.*) to allow too many privileges, be too generous and easygoing toward
   If my aunt continues to ____________________ that child, he may grow into an irresponsible adult.

9. shirk
(shərk)

(*v.*) to avoid or get out of doing work, neglect a duty; to sneak, slink

People who tend to ____________________ their responsibilities are not to be relied upon.

10. veto
(vē' tō)

(*n.*) the power to forbid or prevent; (*v.*) to prohibit, reject

The president decided to ____________________ the bill presented to him by Congress.

Using Context

*For each item, determine whether the **boldface** word from pages 146–147 makes sense in the context of the sentence. Circle the item numbers next to the six sentences in which the words are used correctly.*

1. The hero of the mythical tale set out to find the dragon's **lair** and then capture the enormous beast.

2. I knew that I would **botch** my lines if I was nervous, so I tried to stay calm while waiting to audition for the play.

3. We must analyze why all previous attempts to solve the problem have failed and then **veto** a new approach.

4. Several neighbors volunteered to bring tools and supplies and help rebuild the **dilapidated** barn.

5. Scientists warned that the volcano was **futile** and likely to erupt within days.

6. Anyone who cheats people out of their hard-earned savings is completely **hospitable**.

7. The man I met at lunch is a **notorious** writer; so far, he has published almost 50 novels and more than 200 short stories.

8. It is understandable that you might want to relax and **pamper** yourself after working day and night for several months to complete a project.

9. The library was a **beneficiary** of extra funds this year, thanks to an unexpected surplus in the city's budget.

10. Just for a little while, we decided to **shirk** our duties and enjoy the beautiful spring day.

Choosing the Right Word

*Select the **boldface** word that better completes each sentence. You might refer to the passage on pages 144–145 to see how most of these words are used in context. Note that the choices might be related forms of the Unit words.*

1. We who live in the United States today are the chief (**beneficiaries, lairs**) of the rich heritage of freedom left to us by the framers of the Constitution.

2. Their record is 100 percent consistent—they have managed to (**botch, pamper**) every job they have undertaken.

3. The campaign to eliminate pollution will prove (**futile, hospitable**) unless it has full public support.

4. She was indeed fortunate to find herself working under a person who was (**notorious, hospitable**) to her novel ideas.

5. When he said he would "beard the lion in his (**lair, veto**)," he merely meant that he was going to have it out with the boss.

6. Most Presidents don't like to exercise their (**veto, beneficiary**) power often.

7. Since I was led to believe that she would approve my proposal, I was very much taken aback when it was (**pampered, vetoed**) out of hand.

8. He is (**hospitable, notorious**) for his habit of taking small loans from his best friends and then conveniently forgetting about them.

9. My experience has been that people who cut corners on small matters will also (**shirk, botch**) their obligations.

10. Beneath the (**notorious, dilapidated**) body of the getaway car, there was a powerful, finely tuned motor, capable of reaching high speeds.

11. The sudden thunderstorm made a (**beneficiary, botch**) of the picnic, forcing us to flee for cover and soaking most of our food.

12. I sometimes think that he enjoys being sick and having everyone wait on him, sympathize with him, and (**shirk, pamper**) him.

Completing the Sentence

Choose the word from the word bank that best completes each of the following sentences. Write the correct word or form of the word in the space provided.

beneficiary	dilapidated	hospitable	notorious	shirk
botch	futile	lair	pamper	veto

1. He is such a ____________________ liar that no one takes anything he says seriously anymore.

2. Ever since the new tax laws went into effect, there has been speculation as to who the real ____________________ of the changes will be.

3. Though the cabin was a little ____________________ when we bought it, we were able to spruce it up without going to a great deal of expense.

4. The inexperienced assistant ____________________ the business letter he was trying to compose and had to rewrite it.

5. A sitting President can ____________________ a measure passed by a majority of Congress, but lawmakers can overrule his decision.

6. As a child she was so ____________________ by her parents that she still seems to think that her wishes should be instantly granted.

7. The animals in the zoo are kept in quarters that are designed to imitate their ____________________ in the wild.

8. I know what it is that I have to do, and you may be certain that I will not ____________________ my duty.

9. Unfortunately, the brave lifeguard's valiant attempts to rescue the drowning swimmer proved ____________________.

10. All the members of that family are such ____________________ people that we are always completely at ease whenever we visit them.

End Set A

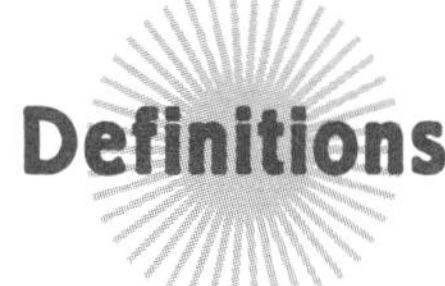

Note the spelling, pronunciation, part(s) of speech, and definition(s) of each of the following words. Then write the appropriate form of the word in the blank space in the illustrative sentence(s) following.

1. bellow (bel′ ō)
(*v.*) to make a sound similar to that of a bull, roar; (*n.*) a loud, angry roar
The wounded buffalo began to ________________ in pain.
The troop commander's ________________ could be heard a mile away.

2. clutter (klət′ ər)
(*v.*) to fill or cover in a disorderly way; (*n.*) a state of disorder, mess
When we moved into our new house, we unloaded the truck and began to ________________ up the dining room with boxes.
Attics are often filled with ________________.

3. dismantle (dis man′ təl)
(*v.*) to take apart; to strip of something
After the final performance, all the actors worked with the stagehands to ________________ the set.

4. farce (färs)
(*n.*) a play filled with ridiculous or absurd happenings; broad or far-fetched humor; a ridiculous sham
The humor in the play was so broad and the plot so ridiculous that the critic termed the play a ________________.

5. grueling (grü′ liŋ)
(*adj.*) very tiring, calling for an extreme effort
After the ________________ climb, two of the mountaineers collapsed from exhaustion.

6. lavish (lav′ ish)
(*adj.*) overly generous, extravagant; abundant; (*v.*) to spend or give freely or without limit
The couple received ________________ wedding gifts from their closest friends.

7. morbid (môr′ bid)
(*adj.*) in an unhealthy mental state, extremely gloomy; caused by or related to disease, unwholesome
The police captain was afraid that the officer was taking a ________________ interest in the crime.

8. parasite (par′ ə sīt)
(*n.*) an organism that lives in or on another organism; one who lives off another person
Uninvited, he hung around with the players so much that the team considered him a real ________________.

9. surplus (sər′ pləs)

(*n.*) an amount beyond what is required, excess; (*adj.*) more than what is needed or expected

Dad was relieved to find that his business had a ______________________ at the end of the year.

The army decided to sell its ______________________ goods to a group of manufacturers.

10. timidity (tə mid′ ə tē)

(*n.*) the state of being easily frightened

The shy child's natural ______________________ had made her afraid to try out for the team.

Using Context

*For each item, determine whether the **boldface** word from pages 150–151 makes sense in the context of the sentence. Circle the item numbers next to the six sentences in which the words are used correctly.*

1. Her **morbid** interest in foreign languages suggests that she may one day work as an interpreter.
2. It turned out we had ordered a **surplus** of food for the party, so we decided to give what was left over to a local shelter.
3. When I realized I had put one part of the bookcase on backward, I had to **dismantle** the whole thing in order to fix the one mistake.
4. He reacts with such intense **farce** whenever anyone criticizes him that he must have some deep-seated insecurities.
5. The melodious **bellow** I heard from the room next to mine was so peaceful that I immediately felt more relaxed.
6. After the **grueling** workout session, I could hardly do anything except sit on the couch for the rest of the night.
7. The **lavish** praise that the writer received for her debut novel made her fear that a second book couldn't possibly be as well-received.
8. As I searched through the **clutter** in my drawers for my passport, I happened to find quite a few knickknacks that I previously thought I had lost forever.
9. It's hard to believe that someone who has changed schools so many times still feels such **timidity** when having to meet new people.
10. She is known as a **parasite** who wastes no time in helping others, regardless of whether she knows them or not.

Choosing the Right Word

*Select the **boldface** word that better completes each sentence. You might refer to the passage on pages 144–145 to see how most of these words are used in context. Note that the choices might be related forms of the Unit words.*

1. The modern TV sitcom developed from the type of broad (**surplus, farce**) that slapstick comedians served up in the 1920s and 1930s.

2. Ever since I was bitten by a stray mutt years ago, I have had a (**morbid, lavish**) fear of all dogs.

3. What a difference between the (**timidity, farce**) of the typical freshman and the know-it-all confidence of a senior!

4. It would be impossible to (**clutter, dismantle**) our system of governmental checks and balances without destroying American democracy.

5. "I discovered a really cool store with all kinds of (**morbid, surplus**) army and navy equipment," Joel told his friends excitedly.

6. The best way to avoid those (**grueling, bellowing**) cram sessions just before the exams is to do your work steadily all term long.

7. When I think back to my days of basic training, I can almost hear the drill sergeant (**lavishing, bellowing**) commands across the field.

8. Even the toughest critics have been (**lavish, grueling**) in their praise of the new movie.

9. After buying all the supplies for the club party, we were delighted to find that we had a grand (**surplus, timidity**) of 65 cents.

10. He amazed us by reaching into the pile of (**clutter, parasites**) on his desk and pulling out the exact piece of paper he wanted.

11. After winning the award for best actress, she joyously (**lavished, dismantled**) praise on everyone who had worked with her on the movie.

12. The courts of many Renaissance princes were filled with (**parasites, clutter**), toadies, and other idle hangers-on.

Choose the word from the word bank that best completes each of the following sentences. Write the correct word or form of the word in the space provided.

bellow	dismantle	grueling	morbid	surplus
clutter	farce	lavish	parasite	timidity

1. Why must you ____________________ up your mind with so many trivial and useless scraps of information?

2. Many people both here and abroad seem to have a ____________________ fascination with the tragic fate of the Russian royal family.

3. It is a curious fact of nature that most ____________________ are unable to survive when they are separated from the organisms they feed on.

4. It is hard to believe that a teenager so courageous and capable on a camping trip can show so much ____________________ when invited to a dance.

5. The ____________________ of food produced each year in the United States is desperately needed to feed hungry people all over the world.

6. When I accepted the invitation to join them on the vessel, I didn't realize that I had agreed to help ____________________ the ship.

7. When he realized that he had been tricked by his opponent, he let out a ____________________ of rage that could be heard all over the gym.

8. Since the defendant was never given a chance to prove his innocence, his so-called "trial" was nothing more than a ____________________.

9. They gave me so ____________________ a helping of dinner that for the first time in my life I was unable to polish off the food on my plate.

10. The practice session was so ____________________ that we scarcely had the strength to get to the dressing room and take our showers.

End Set B

Synonyms

*Choose the word or form of the word from this Unit that is the same or most nearly the same in meaning as the **boldface** word or expression in the phrase. Write that word on the line. Use a dictionary if necessary.*

1. will attempt to **halt** the passing of the law ____________
2. a meeting that turned into a **mockery** ____________
3. would hang on like a **leech** ____________
4. the **recipient** of the scholarship ____________
5. weary from an **exhausting** five-mile run ____________
6. had a **grim** sense of humor ____________
7. may **fumble** the assignment if not careful ____________
8. a **glut** of homes available for sale ____________
9. cleaned up the **jumble** of tools in Dad's workroom ____________
10. **showered** her with praise ____________
11. took up acting to overcome his **shyness** ____________
12. **disassemble** the toaster ____________
13. was reluctant to **coddle** the spoiled child any further ____________
14. cautiously inspected the **decayed** old building ____________
15. saw that the wolf had returned to its **hiding place** ____________

Antonyms

*Choose the word or form of the word from this Unit that is most nearly opposite in meaning to the **boldface** word or expression in the phrase. Write that word on the line. Use a dictionary if necessary.*

1. not one to **take on** extra chores ____________
2. **whisper** a command to the soldier ____________
3. made a **successful** attempt ____________
4. a **respectable** politician known for his actions ____________
5. approached in an **unfriendly** manner ____________

Writing: Words in Action

Do people care too much about their appearance, or is the quest for physical improvement a healthy impulse? Consider both sides of the issue, and then write at least two paragraphs for each side. Include at least one detail from the passage (pages 144–145) for each side. Use three or more words from this Unit.

Vocabulary in Context

*Some of the words you have studied in this Unit appear in **boldface** type. Read the passage below, and then circle the letter of the correct answer for each word as it is used in context.*

Greene Vardiman Black was born on a serene farm in Illinois in 1836. He liked to **shirk** some of his studies at school, preferring to hunt, fish, and scamper in the woods instead; he walked to each animal's **lair** in order to hunt deer and wolves. Although his family thought that his pastimes were a **farce**, they enabled him to develop the observational skills that would be crucial in his career.

When Black was 17, he moved in with his brother, who was a doctor in Clayton, Illinois. For four years, he was the **beneficiary** of his brother's expertise in medicine and anatomy. After this term, he decided to **veto** the study of medicine in favor of dentistry. He studied dentistry with Dr. J. C. Speer, who practiced in Mt. Sterling, Illinois. In 1856, Black established a reputable dental practice in Jacksonville, Illinois. Although he didn't follow formal educational channels, Black received several honorary degrees—D.D.S., M.D., Sc.D., and LL.D.—which many scientists envied.

Black wanted to elevate the mechanical practice of dentistry to a scientific and highly skilled profession. He invented the cord driven dental engine with a foot motor in 1870, and he developed a system to classify dental caries that is still in use today. He also wrote about bone infections and lesions, caused by a bacteria or a **parasite**, that can develop after root canals. These advancements helped Black earn the nickname "the father of modern dentistry."

---

1. In paragraph 1, what does the word **shirk** suggest about Black?

a. He was studious.
b. He was intelligent.
c. He was sneaky.
d. He was sensitive.

2. What does the word **lair** most likely mean as it is used in paragraph 1?

a. hideout
b. predator
c. prey
d. offspring

3. The word **farce** means about the same as

a. a credible belief
b. a ridiculous sham
c. an immature idea
d. a dishonest plan

4. Which word means the same as **beneficiary** as it is used in paragraph 2?

a. opponent
b. provider
c. partner
d. recipient

5. **Veto** comes from the Latin word **vetare**. **Vetare** most likely means

a. to forbid
b. to observe
c. to enhance
d. to select

6. What is the meaning of **parasite** as it is used in paragraph 3?

a. a host
b. a virus
c. an organism
d. a disease

UNIT 11

*Read the following passage, taking note of the **boldface** words and their contexts. These words are among those you will be studying in Unit 11. It may help you to complete the exercises in this Unit if you refer to the way the words are used below.*

The Babe Is Here

<Magazine Article>

September 17, 1954
By Mitch P. J. Cunningham IV for
Sport and Game magazine

You can hear a pin drop. It's almost a **stalemate** among several long-time rivals. Can Babe pull it off? She eyes the eighteenth hole, extends her arms for the downswing, and—it's a hole in one! Babe Didrikson Zaharias, queen of the fairway, has triumphed, and the crowd goes wild. Her fans rush forward, and there's confusion and **havoc** on the greens.

There's a poignancy to this win because Babe, a cofounder of the LPGA (Ladies Professional Golf Association), was diagnosed with cancer at the height of her fame. Doctors said she'd never play again, but they should have known not to bet against this indomitable woman. After **mulling** it over for about a split second, she figured she wasn't going to let a little thing like a serious illness **mar** her remarkable athletic career. She had other fish to fry. She made a **pact** with her husband and manager, former pro wrestler George Zaharias, after undergoing surgery. She swore she'd keep the door **ajar** to return, and return she did. Friends **implored** her to slow down. What did she have to prove? But Babe wasn't buying it. She won the Serbin Women's Open Tournament less than a year after surgery. As she's been heard to say before a tournament: "The Babe's here. Who's coming in second?"

It seems as if Port Arthur, Texas, native Mildred "Babe" Didrikson has the Midas touch when it comes to athletics. Is there any sport at which she doesn't excel? Her many talents are legendary and practically **innumerable**. Most agree she's the best woman athlete alive. In fact, in 1949 the Associated Press voted her the greatest female athlete of the half-century, and she's won a gaggle of other awards and lifetime achievement honors. No one comes close to this lady with the incredible gifts and **gigantic** heart of a champion.

The **narrative** of Babe's life reads like something out of a Hollywood movie script, complete with brash **dialogue** between Babe and whoever

Babe Didrikson Zaharias was one of the greatest golfers who ever lived, shown here in 1947.

tries to get in her way. Born in 1911 to Norwegian immigrants, she displayed exceptional physical prowess at a tender age. She excelled in baseball, swimming, diving, tennis, and bowling. Friends started calling her Babe—as in Babe Ruth—after she hit five home runs in one baseball game. She was an All-American high school basketball player. Then she became a bona fide star at the 1932 Summer Olympics, taking home two gold medals in track and field. (Some say she should have won a third for the high jump, but her **infamous** and illegal style of diving shoulders-first over the bar cost her first place.) Many would have **wilted** under the pressure, but Babe never weakened. At this point, she could have rested on her laurels. Any of these accomplishments would have been more than **adequate** for the average woman (or man, come to think of it).

But Babe is no average woman. She was introduced to golf in 1935—and golf has never been the same since! She started winning titles in 1940, continued her unparalleled run, and completed the Grand Slam for women's golf in 1950, winning the U.S. Open, the Titleholders Championship, and the Women's Western Open. We'd be **lax** if we didn't mention that Babe is working on her autobiography, due out next year. The little girl from Port Arthur has done plenty to advance the ideals of women's sports and win the admiration of millions.

Babe Didrikson Zaharias was a champion in many different sports, here seen winning the hurdle event at the 1932 Olympics in Los Angeles.

Babe Didrikson Zaharias won 82 tournaments in her golfing career.

Audio

For iWords and audio passages, go to **SadlierConnect.com.**

Definitions

Note the spelling, pronunciation, part(s) of speech, and definition(s) of each of the following words. Then write the appropriate form of the word in the blank space in the illustrative sentence(s) following.

1. ajar (ə jär′)
(*adj., adv.*) partly open
That night, the children foolishly left the back gate ______________, and the dog escaped.

2. emblem (em′ bləm)
(*n.*) a symbol, sign, token
Like the heart, the red rose is an ______________ of love.

3. havoc (hav′ ək)
(*n.*) very great destruction, ruin; great confusion and disorder
The monkey created ______________ at the fair as soon as it broke from its leash.

4. implore (im plôr′)
(*v.*) to beg earnestly for
The attorney proceeded to ______________ the judge to show his client mercy.

5. infamous (in′ fə məs)
(*adj.*) very wicked; disgraceful, shameful
Because of the outlaw's ______________ deeds, the town was offering a large bounty for his capture.

6. lax (laks)
(*adj.*) not strict, careless; lacking discipline; not tense, relaxed
Some players took advantage of the new coach's somewhat ______________ control of the team.

7. mull (məl)
(*v.*) to think about, ponder; to grind or mix; to heat and flavor with spices
The governor had some time to ______________ over the bill before signing it into law.

8. overture (o′ vər chůr)
(*n.*) an opening move toward negotiation or action; a proposal or offer; an introductory section or part
Our family enjoyed the ______________ to the opera better than the rest of it.

9. stalemate (stāl′ māt)
(*n.*) a situation in which further action by either of two opponents is impossible; (*v.*) to bring to a standstill

The negotiations ended in a ________________, as both sides refused to budge on the main issue.

Recent aggression on the part of one nation threatened to ________________ the peace talks.

10. vindictive (vin dik′ tiv)
(*adj.*) bearing a grudge, feeling or showing a strong tendency toward revenge

The mayor was so ________________ that he threatened to sue the newspaper for its unflattering remarks about his administration.

*For each item, determine whether the **boldface** word from pages 158–159 makes sense in the context of the sentence. Circle the item numbers next to the six sentences in which the words are used correctly.*

1. Please leave the door **ajar** because our hands will be full of packages when we come in.
2. The novel, which received little attention when it was published in 1851, remained **infamous** for many years and became known as a classic in the mid-twentieth century.
3. Professor Moriarty is a **vindictive** master criminal whose goal is to destroy his archenemy—the famous detective Sherlock Holmes.
4. We need to find out how much it will cost to have our team **emblem** printed on T-shirts and banners.
5. The cleaning crew swept the marble stairs and then polished the brass railings in front of the embassy, leaving them clean and **lax**.
6. If you are an undecided voter, you still have several weeks to observe the candidates and **mull** over your decision.
7. The attractive **havoc** above the building's entryway blocks out the strong afternoon sunlight.
8. Thanks to an **overture** in sales, the company was able to give all employees a bonus.
9. Before going to sleep every night, the twins **implore** their father to read them a bedtime story.
10. The landlord and tenants cannot agree on who should pay for the new bicycle rack, so the situation is now a **stalemate**.

Set A

Choosing the Right Word

*Select the **boldface** word that better completes each sentence. You might refer to the passage on pages 156–157 to see how most of these words are used in context. Note that the choices might be related forms of the Unit words.*

1. For many years Benedict Arnold served his country faithfully, but then he disgraced his name for all time by an (**ajar, infamous**) act of treason.

2. I wish you had (**implored, mulled**) over all the pros and cons before you made your final decision.

3. Jorge and Louise both want to be friends again, but somehow their sincere efforts have been (**stalemated, implored**).

4. Some parents are quite strict with their children; others are somewhat (**lax, infamous**) and permissive.

5. Contract talks have been stalled for weeks, and nothing either side has suggested can seem to break the (**stalemate, overture**).

6. In spite of all the criticism, our flag still stands throughout most of the world as a(n) (**stalemate, emblem**) of justice and freedom.

7. Instead of continuing to (**mull, implore**) over the injustices that people have done to you, forget about the past and concentrate on the future.

8. The blustery winds on that cold November day played (**havoc, overture**) with my hair.

9. As long as the door to compromise is even slightly (**ajar, vindictive**), there is a chance that we will be able to reach an understanding.

10. I was a little miffed when my polite (**stalemates, overtures**) of friendship were so rudely and nastily rejected.

11. Since I am willing to contribute to any worthy cause, there is no need to (**mull, implore**) me for aid in such an emotional way.

12. After World War II, the United States was not (**vindictive, lax**) toward its former enemies but tried to help them recover and rebuild.

Completing the Sentence

Choose the word from the word bank that best completes each of the following sentences. Write the correct word or form of the word in the space provided.

ajar	havoc	infamous	mull	stalemate
emblem	implore	lax	overture	vindictive

1. The flood had wrought such ____________________ that the governor of the state declared the stricken region a disaster area.

2. A white dove holding an olive branch in its beak is often used as a(n) ____________________ of peace.

3. By entering into World War I, the United States broke the ____________________ on the Western Front and tipped the balance in favor of an Allied victory.

4. Though some of Verdi's operas begin with short preludes, for others he composed full-length ____________________.

5. She ____________________ the doctor to tell her frankly how badly her son had been hurt.

6. Since I have never done him any harm, I don't understand why he should take such a(n) ____________________ attitude toward me.

7. Can any punishment be too severe for someone who has been guilty of such a(n) ____________________ crime?

8. No one questions the honesty and good intentions of the mayor, but he has been criticized for being ____________________ in carrying out his duties.

9. Let me have some time to ____________________ over your proposal before I give you a definite answer.

10. Because the front door was ____________________, the cat strolled into the living room.

End Set A

Definitions

Note the spelling, pronunciation, part(s) of speech, and definition(s) of each of the following words. Then write the appropriate form of the word in the blank space in the illustrative sentence(s) following.

1. adequate (ad′ ə kwət)
(*adj.*) sufficient, enough
Be sure to allow ____________________ time to check in at the airport.

2. dialogue (dī′ ə läg)
(*n.*) a conversation between two or more people; an interchange of opinions and ideas, free discussion
The witty ____________________ in the play kept the audience amused.

3. gigantic (jī gan′ tik)
(*adj.*) huge, giant, immense
When it fell to Earth, the meteorite made a ____________________ hole in the ground.

4. hearth (härth)
(*n.*) the floor of a fireplace; the fireside as a symbol of the home and family
It was our custom to sit by the ____________________ and listen to my grandfather's stories.

5. innumerable (i nüm′ ə rə bəl)
(*adj.*) too many to count, without number
The landlord heard ____________________ complaints about the noisy new tenant.

6. mar (mär)
(*v.*) to spoil, damage, injure
Spilled cleaning fluid will surely ____________________ the wooden tabletop.

7. misdemeanor (mis di mē′ nər)
(*n.*) a crime or offense that is less serious than a felony; any minor misbehavior or misconduct
He was not only fined for the ____________________ but also sentenced to thirty days in jail.

8. narrative (nar′ ə tiv)
(*n.*) a story, detailed report; (*adj.*) having the quality or the nature of a story
The ____________________ of the West African captive gives us a vivid picture of the horrors aboard a slave ship.
Henry Wadsworth Longfellow is considered a ____________________ poet because of the stories he tells in his poems.

9. pact (pakt) — (*n.*) an agreement, treaty

All the nations signed the ____________ after the war in an effort to ensure world peace.

10. wilt (wilt) — (*v.*) to become limp and drooping (as a flower), wither; to lose strength and vigor

Intense heat or lack of water will ____________ the flowers.

For each item, determine whether the ***boldface*** *word from pages 162–163 makes sense in the context of the sentence. Circle the item numbers next to the six sentences in which the words are used correctly.*

1. Although I knew blue whales were large, I was not quite expecting to see such a **gigantic** creature right before my eyes.

2. Since my friend and I disagree on a few topics, we have made a **pact** to not discuss them with one another so that we don't argue.

3. Although I began to tire toward the end of the race, the sight of the finish line was enough to **wilt** my spirits, and so I sprinted toward it as quickly as I could.

4. While you may not think that committing a **misdemeanor** here and there is cause for concern, such actions can eventually lead to more serious crimes.

5. Looking at the rundown cabin, it was obvious that the haggard old man had an **innumerable** amount of money.

6. I found the conversation so **adequate** that I feared I would not be able to stifle a yawn.

7. The public figure worried that recent news of a scandal involving him would **mar** his reputation forever.

8. She is such a talented storyteller that she can turn even her boring, everyday activities into an exciting and hilarious **narrative**.

9. After sitting in the stuffy lecture hall for hours, it was a relief to escape to the **hearth** right outside of the building and breathe in some fresh air.

10. The theme of the movie seemed promising, but I was distracted by the awkward and stilted **dialogue** between the two leads.

Choosing the Right Word

Select the ***boldface*** *word that better completes each sentence. You might refer to the passage on pages 156–157 to see how most of these words are used in context. Note that the choices might be related forms of the Unit words.*

1. British enlistment posters in World War I assured young men that they would be fighting for "king and country, (**hearth, pact**) and home."

2. Though jaywalking may be considered a (**misdemeanor, dialogue**), murder is definitely not!

3. The facts of history cannot always be arranged in the form of a smooth and logical (**pact, narrative**).

4. I will not allow our long and much cherished friendship to be (**marred, wilted**) by this unfortunate misunderstanding.

5. "(**Adequate, innumerable**) is simply not good enough," the company president said. "We want to be the best in our field."

6. I prefer (**narrative, dialogue**) fiction to drama or poetry.

7. The wonders of nature are as (**innumerable, adequate**) as the grains of sand on the seashore.

8. Instead of resorting at once to armed force, the two nations resolved the conflict by entering into a diplomatic (**dialogue, misdemeanor**).

9. As I look over your record, I get the impression that your background in math and science is not (**adequate, innumerable**) for an engineering course.

10. Our high hopes for an easy victory (**wilted, marred**) away to nothing as we watched our opponents steadily increase their lead over us.

11. Her insistence on studying the terms of our tutoring agreement made me think that I'd signed a (**pact, hearth**) with a lawyer.

12. The man has such a(n) (**adequate, gigantic**) ego that absolutely nothing ever seems to fluster, faze, or deflate him.

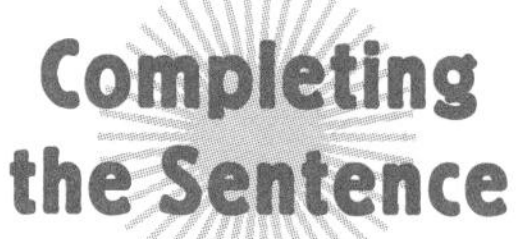

Choose the word from the word bank that best completes each of the following sentences. Write the correct word or form of the word in the space provided.

adequate	gigantic	innumerable	misdemeanor	pact
dialogue	hearth	mar	narrative	wilt

1. One careless mistake can seriously ________________ an otherwise perfect record.
2. "The Highwayman" by Alfred Noyes is a(n) ________________ poem that tells the story of a woman who sacrifices her life for her sweetheart.
3. As you will learn, in most operettas, the musical numbers are connected to one another by spoken ________________.
4. You cannot expect to discipline a group of teenagers by making a capital offense of every ________________.
5. Though Hitler's Germany and Stalin's Russia were bitter enemies, the two countries signed a nonaggression ________________ in 1939.
6. Before you leave, be absolutely sure that your supplies of food and water are ________________ for an eight-day journey across the desert.
7. Though my sister started out looking as fresh as a daisy, she began to ________________ noticeably after only five minutes in that humidity.
8. On our trip to northern California, we felt very small and unimportant as we stood beside the ________________ redwood trees.
9. Who has not gazed with awe at the ________________ stars that fill the sky on a clear summer night!
10. The smoke from the logs burning on the ________________ curled slowly upward into the chimney.

End Set B

Synonyms

*Choose the word or form of the word from this Unit that is the same or most nearly the same in meaning as the **boldface** word or expression in the phrase. Write that word on the line. Use a dictionary if necessary.*

1. to treat the crime as a **little mishap** ____________
2. wears an **insignia** on his collar ____________
3. signed the **accord** that would end the fighting ____________
4. **countless** flakes of snow ____________
5. a lively **discourse** between friends ____________
6. **beseech** the class to be quiet ____________
7. **considered** her response before speaking ____________
8. locked in a political **standoff** ____________
9. had a **scandalous** reputation ____________
10. the elephant's **enormous** feet ____________
11. picked up where the **anecdote** left off ____________
12. so **negligent** in her duties ____________
13. began to **hang downward** in the extreme heat ____________
14. a trash heap that would **deface** the view ____________
15. a peaceful scene by the **home fire** ____________

Antonyms

*Choose the word or form of the word from this Unit that is most nearly opposite in meaning to the **boldface** word or expression in the phrase. Write that word on the line. Use a dictionary if necessary.*

1. the lovely **conclusion** of the symphony ____________
2. a truly **merciful** person ____________
3. an **insufficient** amount of evidence ____________
4. the **calm** after the storm ____________
5. left the door **wide open** ____________

Writing: Words in Action

Babe Didrikson Zaharias's domination of several sports made her a cultural icon. Write an essay stating why you think sports heroes are so important to Americans. Support your opinion with examples from your reading (pages 156–157), studies, and personal experience. Use three or more words from this Unit.

Vocabulary in Context

*Some of the words you have studied in this Unit appear in **boldface** type. Read the passage below, and then circle the letter of the correct answer for each word as it is used in context.*

The city-state of Elis in southern Greece was the birthplace of the Olympic Games. The first Games were held in 776 BCE, and every four years for the next 1,169 years the finest male athletes in all of Greece gathered in the Elean town of Olympia to compete for crowns of olive leaves, each an **emblem** of victory.

Track and field contests filled stadiums all over Greece. The Olympics were the first and the greatest, but similar contests were held in every city-state. The Heraean Games (or "Heraea"), however, were different from every other contest in Greece. The competitors were all female.

The Heraea were held every four years. They occupied the Olympic stadium for the month before the Olympics. Their contest was not, however, an **overture** to the main event. Further, female athletes did not feel resentful or **vindictive** toward their male counterparts. The discipline was not more **lax** for women than for men. The female athletes conducted themselves at all times in a spirit of friendly rivalry. They competed over several age groups, and participants were all unmarried. It would have been a **misdemeanor** for a married woman to participate, since participation would have kept her from **hearth** and home.

According to myth, the Games were founded by Queen Hippodameia of Pisa (later part of Elis) to celebrate her wedding to Pelops, a grandson of Zeus. Just as the Olympic Games were dedicated to Zeus, the Heraea were dedicated to Hera, the wife of Zeus, and the goddess and protector of women.

---

1. **Emblem** comes from the Latin word **emblema**. **Emblema** most likely means
   a. evidence
   b. reward
   c. ceremonial headgear
   d. raised ornament

2. What is the meaning of **overture** as it is used in paragraph 3?
   a. a piece of music
   b. a lead-in
   c. the beginning
   d. the final event

3. The word **vindictive** means about the same as
   a. accusing
   b. malicious
   c. accommodating
   d. envious

4. What is the meaning of **lax**, as it is used in paragraph 3?
   a. strict
   b. self-imposed
   c. loose
   d. easy

5. Which word means the same as **misdemeanor** as it is used in paragraph 3?
   a. error
   b. inappropriate
   c. misjudgment
   d. crime

6. What does the word **hearth** most likely mean as it is used in paragraph 3?
   a. fireplace
   b. warmth
   c. a symbol of home
   d. a place of solitude

UNIT 12

*Read the following passage, taking note of the **boldface** words and their contexts. These words are among those you will be studying in Unit 12. It may help you to complete the exercises in this Unit if you refer to the way the words are used below.*

Hero from the Wrong Side of the Track Retires

<Profile>

by Chester Byron Langdon
November 11, 1940

The Great Depression had darkened almost every door in this country, and war clouds were gathering on the European horizon. America was hungry for a hero. Then came a horse named Seabiscuit, whose looks hid the champion he would become. He was knobby-kneed and undersized, and had a laid-back, **leisurely** demeanor. But he hadn't a trace of a **malady** where it counts in a champion—his heart. His heart **abounded** in courage and overflowed with determination.

Foaled in 1933, Seabiscuit grew up in Kentucky. His performance in his first races was mediocre—hard work at a young age had made him **lethargic**, and in 1936, his owners sold the tired colt to Charles S. Howard. Howard, a wealthy businessman, had pioneered the sale of automobiles in California. Howard formed an unorthodox team: Seabiscuit's new trainer was Tom Smith, known for his reluctance to speak, and Johnny "Red" Pollard was Seabiscuit's jockey. Most people in the racing world did not know that Pollard was blind in one eye, thus depriving him of bifocal vision and depth perception.

From left to right: Tom Smith, George Woolf, Seabiscuit, and C.S. Howard

The team led a **nomadic** existence, escorting their horse to races in the eastern states, the Midwest, and California. Against the odds, Seabiscuit's record improved, and he quickly gathered increasing attention in the racing community. Howard was a born marketer, a Western-bred underdog challenging the East Coast racing establishment. It was just the role that millions of Americans wanted a winning horse to play. Amid the **turmoil** and confusion

of the Depression, down and out and starved for hope, Seabiscuit's fans saw in him a gritty fighter. The horse became a celebrity almost overnight: "Seabiscuit-itis" swept the nation. A huge **cache** of press clippings devoted to the thoroughbred showed that Seabiscuit, at one point, enjoyed more publicity than President Franklin D. Roosevelt.

But, as the saying goes, trouble rides a fast horse, and it caught up with this racing team. In early 1938, jockey Pollard fell from another horse and shattered his collarbone in a **heartrending** accident that kept him from riding. The same year, with Pollard sidelined, the **quest** for a match-race against War Admiral, a scion of the Eastern horse-racing establishment, came to an exciting end. Pimlico Racecourse, near Baltimore, announced it would host the "match of the century" on November 1, 1938. A new jockey, George Woolf, would pilot Seabiscuit in the most important contest of both of their careers.

The outcome was sensational. Seabiscuit beat the favorite by four lengths—about 11 yards—to the delight of 40,000 fans at the track and an estimated radio audience of 40 million people. Never a **braggart**, Pollard drily remarked from his hospital bed that his horse had turned War Admiral into a rear admiral.

Seabiscuit makes a rear admiral out of War Admiral in their famous match race.

In the winner's circle after the match of the century

In early 1940, Seabiscuit pulled a ligament and left the track to rest in the quiet **seclusion** of Howard's ranch. It was said he would never race again. Howard and Smith, however, did not become **despondent**; they believed in their horse. And Seabiscuit had one more race to claim: the coveted Santa Anita Derby in California, with its $100,000 prize. Seabiscuit, with Pollard back in the saddle, came from behind to win, setting a record track time and **reinforcing** his **status** as the country's greatest racehorse. No wonder Seabiscuit had become an American legend. Now he will retire permanently at Howard's ranch to enjoy the lazy, **mellow** life he deserves.

Audio

For iWords and audio passages, go to **SadlierConnect.com**.

Definitions

Note the spelling, pronunciation, part(s) of speech, and definition(s) of each of the following words. Then write the appropriate form of the word in the blank space in the illustrative sentence(s) following.

1. abound (ə bou̇nd′)

(*v.*) to be plentiful, be filled

Lush fruit trees ____________________ in the orchards of central California.

2. clarification (klar ə fə kā′ shən)

(*n.*) the act of making clear or understandable, an explanation

Reporters asked for a ____________________ of the politician's statement so that they could accurately report her position.

3. leisurely (lē′ zhər lē)

(*adj.*) unhurried, taking plenty of time; (*adv.*) in an easygoing or unhurried way

My parents enjoy taking a ____________________ stroll through the park on a Sunday afternoon.

We ate ____________________ and spent hours talking about old times.

4. malady (mal′ əd ē)

(*n.*) a sickness, illness, disease, disorder

Rheumatic fever, usually a childhood ____________________, can cause permanent damage to the heart.

5. nomadic (nō ma′ dik)

(*adj.*) wandering, moving about from place to place

Many groups in the desert live a ____________________ life, traveling from place to place in search of water and grazing land.

6. piecemeal (pēs′ mēl)

(*adj.*) one piece at a time; (*adv.*) gradually

The committee's ____________________ approach to the problem was taking more time and money than the school board could afford.

Patchwork quilts are sewn ____________________.

7. quest (kwest)

(*n.*) a search, hunt; (*v.*) to search, seek, ask

In ____________________ of a safe water route to the Pacific, Lewis and Clark journeyed more than three thousand miles.

Diplomats ____________________ for peaceful solutions to global problems.

8. random (ran′ dəm)

(*adj.*) by chance, not planned or prearranged; irregular

According to a ____________________ sampling of voters, Proposition 10 will be approved by a wide margin.

9. reinforce (rē in fôrs′) (*v.*) to make stronger with new materials or support
They used steel beams to ______________ the structure of the building.

10. status (stā′ təs) (*n.*) a person's condition or position in the eyes of the law; relative rank or standing, especially in society; prestige
Winning the prestigious book award boosted the young writer's literary ______________.

*For each item, determine whether the **boldface** word from pages 170–171 makes sense in the context of the sentence. Circle the item numbers next to the six sentences in which the words are used correctly.*

1. Is there anything better than spending a **leisurely** hour or two sitting under a tree and reading a good book?
2. Doctors did not doubt that the symptoms of the area's residents were real, but they could not identify the **malady** that was causing them.
3. The wooden fence they are building will **abound** their property and also keep their dog from running away.
4. No matter how much you would like to think that we are in control, you must admit that sometimes a **random** event can change the course of a person's life.
5. Because more seats are needed for the growing number of fans who want to attend games, the stadium is undergoing a **clarification**.
6. When they reached their early thirties, my aunt and uncle became tired of their **nomadic** existence and decided to settle down.
7. The crowd cheered wildly when the runner won the race not only **piecemeal** but in world-record time.
8. The cold, rainy weather **reinforced** our plans to spend the day relaxing at the beach.
9. Did you know that at one time in England only people of royal **status** were allowed to wear purple?
10. The Spanish invasion of the Americas during the 1500s was driven by a **quest** for gold.

Set A

Choosing the Right Word

*Select the **boldface** word that better completes each sentence. You might refer to the passage on pages 168–169 to see how most of these words are used in context. Note that the choices might be related forms of the Unit words.*

1. (**Nomadic, Piecemeal**) groups of horse breeders still wander the plains of Central Asia in search of pasturage for their herds.

2. For weeks, a gang of muggers wandered the streets aimlessly, choosing their victims at (**random, piecemeal**) from those who happened by.

3. The president went on the air to inform the general public of the present (**malady, status**) of the negotiations with the enemy.

4. The eternal (**quest, malady**) for youth and beauty explains the huge sales of cosmetics, to men as well as to women.

5. We repaired the house (**randomly, piecemeal**), doing one small task after another.

6. Over the years, I have learned one thing about rumors: Where the facts are few, fictions (**abound, clarify**).

7. They drove (**piecemeal, leisurely**) through the countryside, taking time to view hills, woods, and meadows full of blooming wildflowers.

8. My experience on my summer job has (**reinforced, abounded**) many of the lessons I learned in the classroom.

9. Instead of such (**leisurely, piecemeal**) efforts to prevent air pollution, we need a unified campaign that will be continued for as long as necessary.

10. As I was in no hurry to get where I was going, I decided to set a rather (**random, leisurely**) pace for myself.

11. I believe that education, understanding, and experience provide the only cure for the (**malady, status**) of prejudice.

12. Our present policy appears to be so contradictory that I believe some (**clarification, quest**) of it is in order.

Completing the Sentence

Choose the word from the word bank that best completes each of the following sentences. Write the correct word or form of the word in the space provided.

abound	**leisurely**	**nomadic**	**quest**	**reinforce**
clarification	**malady**	**piecemeal**	**random**	**status**

1. Arthritis is a(n) ____________________ that attacks many millions of people, especially in middle and old age.

2. Many homeless people now lead essentially ____________________ existences on the streets of our major cities.

3. The lake so ____________________ with trout and pickerel that even a person with my limited skill in fishing can catch them easily.

4. Every once in a while, I like to take time out from my busy schedule to have a(n) ____________________ dinner with old friends.

5. Instead of trying to decide which applicants were best suited for the job, he selected two at ____________________.

6. Most detectives solve crimes in a(n) ____________________ fashion, as clues come to light, rather than all at once.

7. Though Ponce de León's ____________________ for the Fountain of Youth proved futile, he did explore Florida and claim it as territory for the Spanish.

8. When I first entered this country, I was classified as a "resident alien," but my ____________________ has changed since then.

9. At first, when I couldn't make out what she wanted me to do, I asked her for some ____________________ of her instructions.

10. In order to prevent the bridge from collapsing, it has been necessary to ____________________ its girders and foundations.

End Set A

Definitions

Note the spelling, pronunciation, part(s) of speech, and definition(s) of each of the following words. Then write the appropriate form of the word in the blank space in the illustrative sentence(s) following.

1. braggart (brag′ ərt)
(*n.*) a boaster; (*adj.*) boastful in a loud, annoying way
There seems to be a __________________ in every family, who boasts about his or her achievements and worth.
Greek mythology is filled with __________________ gods and heroes who take great pride in their deeds and skills.

2. cache (kash)
(*n.*) a hiding place; something hidden or stored
We found a __________________ of canned food hidden under the stairs in the cellar.

3. despondent (di spän′ dənt)
(*adj.*) sad, without hope, discouraged
The doctor was __________________ over the loss of his patient and dear friend.

4. embezzle (em bez′ əl)
(*v.*) to steal property entrusted to one's care
The senator's aide lost his job when he was caught trying to __________________ campaign funds.

5. heartrending (härt′ ren diŋ)
(*adj.*) causing mental pain or grief
The survivor told a __________________ story about the shipwreck and the days she spent alone on the island.

6. lethargic (lə thär′ jik)
(*adj.*) unnaturally sleepy; dull, slow moving; indifferent
The twins often become __________________ after eating a large meal at their grandmother's house.

7. mellow (mel′ ō)
(*adj.*) ripe, well-matured; soft, sweet, and rich; gentle, pleasant; (*v.*) to become gentle and sweet
Hawaii is known for its __________________ fruit, all of which is ripe and juicy.
Mom continued to hope that her upstart brother would __________________ with age and experience.

8. rant (rant)
(*v.*) to speak wildly and noisily; (*n.*) loud, violent talk
When the speaker began to __________________ like a rabble-rouser, the crowd shouted him down.
Listening to the __________________ of that radio personality makes me want to give up on talk shows.

9. seclusion (si klü′ zhən) (*n.*) isolation from others, solitude
Some actors choose to live in ________________, away from the prying eyes of journalists.

10. turmoil (tər′ moil) (*n.*) a state of great confusion or disorder; mental strain or agitation
For many years after the Civil War, the South remained a society in ________________.

Using Context

For each item, determine whether the ***boldface*** *word from pages 174–175 makes sense in the context of the sentence. Circle the item numbers next to the six sentences in which the words are used correctly.*

1. Her **despondent** attitude is always able to cheer me up even in the gloomiest of situations.

2. It is bad enough to be a **braggart**, but so much worse to be one who hasn't actually accomplished anything worth boasting about.

3. The audience was in **turmoil** after the show's last number, as they cheered for the cast and asked for an encore.

4. I don't usually cry during movies, but the **heartrending** story of star-crossed lovers was enough to move me to tears.

5. When I heard the **mellow** sounds coming from the restaurant next door on my first night in my new home, I immediately regretted moving to such a noisy neighborhood.

6. In case of a weather event that leaves us without power for weeks, my mother has a **cache** of bottled water in the basement.

7. After a few days of complete **seclusion**, I felt recharged and prepared to reenter society.

8. I thought it would be a pleasant day to study outside, but as soon as I sat down a mosquito began to **embezzle** me nonstop until eventually I went back indoors.

9. Although it is clear that you are passionate about this subject, delivering a **rant** about all of your frustrations is not the best way to get your point across.

10. A few days into the heat wave, even the birds seemed **lethargic**, giving halfhearted chirps and flying a little more slowly than usual.

Set B

Choosing the Right Word

*Select the **boldface** word that better completes each sentence. You might refer to the passage on pages 168–169 to see how most of these words are used in context. Note that the choices might be related forms of the Unit words.*

1. Why would a world-famous writer choose to live in the (**turmoil, seclusion**) of a country village far from the "madding crowd"?

2. At the time of our very public argument, I was angry, but over the years my emotions have (**mellowed, embezzled**).

3. Although she appeared calm and composed, her mind was in (**turmoil, cache**).

4. People who waste the natural resources of this country are in a sense (**embezzling, mellowing**) the wealth of future generations.

5. The least useful thing you could do at this moment is to deliver a long, loud (**rant, turmoil**) against your opponents.

6. Only the fact that they cannot see the seriousness of the emergency can explain their (**lethargic, despondent**) response to our appeal for help.

7. As soon as I opened the book, I realized that I had stumbled on a rich (**cache, braggart**) of useful information for my report.

8. There is a great difference between being quietly confident of your own ability and being an obnoxious (**rant, braggart**).

9. Though he (**rants, embezzles**) and raves about the problems of the world, he has little to offer in the way of solutions to them.

10. In the (**heartrending, lethargic**) conclusion of the film, the hero dies in the arms of his beloved friend.

11. People say that Brianna is a (**mellow, heartrending**) person, but I've seen her lose her temper too often to believe them.

12. Many doctors believe that when sick people become (**heartrending, despondent**) over their health, it is more difficult for them to recover.

Completing the Sentence

Choose the word from the word bank that best completes each of the following sentences. Write the correct word or form of the word in the space provided.

braggart	**despondent**	**heartrending**	**mellow**	**seclusion**
cache	**embezzle**	**lethargic**	**rant**	**turmoil**

1. The two brothers are both fine athletes, but one is quiet and modest while the other is an awful ________________.

2. The tenor's voice was rich and ________________, but the baritone's sounded somewhat harsh and unpleasant.

3. After putting up with the noise and confusion of life in the big city all week, I enjoy the ________________ of my mountain retreat on weekends.

4. Apparently, the man could pay off his staggering gambling debts only by ________________ funds from the company that employed him.

5. It's natural for you to feel a little ________________ over not getting the job, but don't let that prevent you from applying for other positions.

6. The park is always full of soapbox orators ________________ about the inequality of government or society.

7. Yesterday, I read a truly ________________ account of the plight of millions of people suffering from the effects of a severe famine.

8. During warm months, foxes bury many animals they have killed, with the result that they have ________________ to tide them over in the winter.

9. Although I am always full of energy in the morning, I start to become a little ________________ as the day wears on.

10. The ________________ of the French Revolution and the Napoleonic Era was succeeded by 100 years of relative peace and quiet in Europe.

End Set B

Synonyms

*Choose the word or form of the word from this Unit that is the same or most nearly the same in meaning as the **boldface** word or expression in the phrase. Write that word on the line. Use a dictionary if necessary.*

1. rehearsed the play **little by little** ________
2. was caught up in the **chaos** left by the storm ________
3. is just another conceited **showoff** ________
4. was among the last **roving** groups in Lapland ________
5. the seas **overflow** with fish ________
6. a **heartbreaking** story of loss ________
7. prefers **solitariness** to being in a crowd ________
8. went on a **venture** to find the buried treasure ________
9. walked at a **relaxed** pace ________
10. news that **bolstered** my confidence ________
11. calmed by the **soothing** music ________
12. found a **stockpile** of coins ________
13. suffers from a serious **indisposition** ________
14. achieved a well-regarded **situation** among her peers ________
15. attempted to **make off with** money from the fund ________

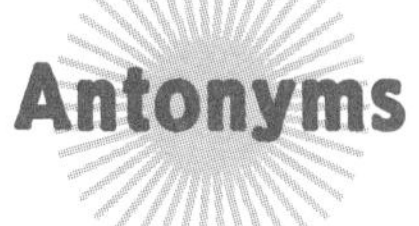

Antonyms

*Choose the word or form of the word from this Unit that is most nearly opposite in meaning to the **boldface** word or expression in the phrase. Write that word on the line. Use a dictionary if necessary.*

1. unwisely chose to **mumble** at the crowd ________
2. witnessed a **deliberate** act of kindness ________
3. **jubilant** over my grades ________
4. feel **energetic** after an afternoon nap ________
5. **confusion** resulting from my explanation ________

Writing: Words in Action

Do you consider a racehorse to be an athlete, like a baseball player or a runner? Write an essay in which you state why you think Seabiscuit was or was not an athlete. Support your opinion with examples from your reading (pages 168–169), observations, or personal experience. Use three or more words from this Unit.

Vocabulary in Context

*Some of the words you have studied in this Unit appear in **boldface** type. Read the passage below, and then circle the letter of the correct answer for each word as it is used in context.*

Not much more than a hundred years ago, the human world **abounded** with horses. In 1900, there were more than 21 million horses and mules in the United States. Today, there are a little more than 3.5 million.

Horses are not the most expressive of animals; or perhaps they are expressive and we just do not understand them. Not many of us possess the kinds of insight and sympathy that make it possible to experience the world as it is experienced by other species. Humans communicate primarily in words. If we fail to understand something, we can demand **clarification** in words, and we can **rant** in words until we get it.

We have bred horses to bear our burdens, to pull our carts, and to speed our plows. We have bred impassive giants to haul our cannons into battle, and to stand immobile while the world blows up at **random** around them. We have even bred miniature miracles of equine power and patience to transport the loot, sometimes **piecemeal**, when we go underground in search of gold, or coal, or some other treasure. In these horses we place our trust. Never, we think, would these animals **embezzle** our riches.

We have bred horses for prowess in racing and jumping. These horses, known as thoroughbreds, are notable for their extraordinary beauty and grace. To win the Kentucky Derby, however, or to be able to function at the level of concentration and precision necessary to win Olympic Gold, a depth of understanding between horse and rider is essential. It is this bond that every spectator recognizes and treasures when watching an equestrian event.

---

1. **Abound** comes from the Latin word **abundare. Abundare** most likely means
   a. to make merry
   b. to occupy
   c. to prosper
   d. to overflow

2. Which word means the same as **clarification** as it is used in paragraph 2?
   a. translation
   b. common sense
   c. explanation
   d. understanding

3. In paragraph 2, what does the use of the word **rant** suggest about us?
   a. We command respect.
   b. We are opinionated.
   c. We demand truth.
   d. We are impatient.

4. What is the meaning of **random** as it is used in paragraph 3?
   a. loudly
   b. leisurely
   c. chaotically
   d. systematically

5. The word **piecemeal** means about the same as
   a. bit by bit
   b. out of sync
   c. confidently
   d. rapidly

6. What does the word **embezzle** most likely mean as it is used in paragraph 3?
   a. steal
   b. cheat
   c. escape
   d. deviate

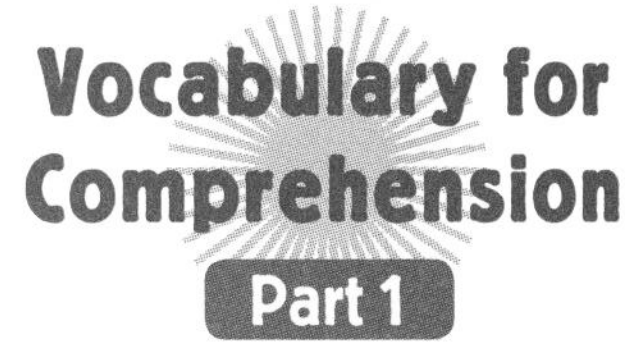

*Read "Champions of Equality," which contains words in **boldface** that appear in Units 10–12. Then answer the questions.*

Champions of Equality

Have you ever heard the term the *Great Migration*? If so, you may know that between 1870 and 1920, hundreds of thousands of African Americans moved from rural areas in the Southeast to the industrialized urban areas in the Northeast and Midwest. For most, this huge migration meant an escape from poverty and the **malady** of discrimination, of being treated unfairly. To these African Americans, the movement north was a **quest** for a better life. Northern factory jobs were a great improvement over farm work.

As more industrial jobs became available during World War I, about half a million African Americans went north. Although their economic **status** improved during the war years, African Americans in both the North and the South were still denied many basic rights. As a result, some notable African Americans rose to the challenge of righting injustices and achieving equal opportunity.

One African American who fought to end injustice was Booker T. Washington. Born enslaved, Washington taught himself to read. Years later, in 1891, he founded the Tuskegee Institute in Alabama. There, students learned skills such as bricklaying, printing, and teaching. These skills would help them improve their lives as they worked peacefully toward equality.

African American women also struggled for justice. Ida B. Wells, for example, strove to end the **notorious** practice of segregation, the separation of African Americans from other groups in society. She spoke against other forms of racial injustice, too. For Wells, her pen and her resolve were her only weapons. As editor of the newspaper *Free Speech*, which she founded in Memphis, Tennessee, Wells fought to end **random** acts of violence against African Americans. "Can you remain silent," she wrote, ". . . when such things are done in your own community and country?"

Mary McLeod Bethune was another champion of African American equality. Born in 1875 to former enslaved people, Bethune became a public leader who worked to improve education and employment opportunities for African Americans. She is best known for founding Bethune-Cookman University in Daytona Beach, Florida. It started as a small private school for African American girls, but Bethune helped it grow into a university through her **innumerable** efforts to promote education. Bethune also became an adviser to President Franklin D. Roosevelt on African American concerns. She once said, "If our people are to fight their way up out of bondage we must arm them with the sword and the shield and buckler of pride—belief in themselves and their possibilities."

As these African American leaders and others lectured across the country, they inspired the growth of the civil rights movement. In fact, even today, their words and deeds motivate organizations to continue the struggle for justice.

1. Based on the evidence in the passage, what is **most likely** the author's purpose in "Champions of Equality"?
   A) to describe African American life in the North from 1870 to 1920
   B) to entertain the reader with several fictional anecdotes
   C) to tell a personal story about the writer's ancestors
   D) to inform the reader about African Americans' early struggles to end injustice

2. Why does the author **most likely** begin the passage with the question in lines 1–2?
   A) to reveal what will be discussed in paragraph 2
   B) to give the central idea of the passage
   C) to provide the focus for paragraph 1
   D) to imply that the reader is lacking knowledge

3. What is the meaning of **malady** as it is used in line 9 of "Champions of Equality"?
   A) humiliation
   B) stigma
   C) affliction
   D) oppression

4. **Part A**
   Which statement **best** provides an inference about African Americans who moved to the North that is supported by the text?
   A) They found everyone was treated fairly.
   B) They soon left to fight World War I.
   C) They continued to experience injustice.
   D) They all worked in factory jobs.

   Part B
   Which sentence from the passage **best** supports your answer to Part A?
   A) "this huge migration meant an escape from poverty" (lines 7–8)
   B) "the movement north was a quest for a better life" (lines 10–12)
   C) "Northern factory jobs were a great improvement" (lines 12–13)
   D) "were still denied many basic rights" (lines 19–20)

5. As used in line 11, what is the meaning of the word **quest**?
   A) search
   B) request
   C) victory
   D) competition

6. Which word is closest in meaning to the word **status** as it is used in line 17?
   A) education
   B) condition
   C) skills
   D) opportunities

7. Which word means the opposite of **notorious** in line 35?
   A) respectable
   B) haphazard
   C) disgraceful
   D) cruel

8. Which statement **best** describes what lines 39–40 add to the reader's understanding of the text?
   A) The sentence shows that Wells gave in to pressure to stop writing.
   B) The sentence implies that Wells used her writing to fight injustice.
   C) The sentence establishes that Wells defended herself against enemies.
   D) The sentence explains that Wells was weak and easily intimidated.

9. What does the word **random** in line 43 suggest about acts of violence against African Americans?
   A) They were planned.
   B) They were brutal.
   C) They were shocking.
   D) They were arbitrary.

10. As used in line 59, what is the meaning of the word **innumerable**?
    A) unbelievable
    B) minor
    C) indifferent
    D) countless

Vocabulary for Comprehension Part 2

Read these passages, which contain words in ***boldface*** *that appear in Units 10–12. Then choose the best answer to each question based on what is stated or implied in the passage(s). You may refer to the passages as often as necessary.*

Questions 1–10 are based on the following passages.

Passage 1

Leaving food on your plate after a meal may not seem like a huge problem. In reality, this habit is part of a larger issue about food waste. In the United States, 40 percent of food is thrown out. That percentage amounts to 20 pounds of food per person every month.

Up to 10 percent of food purchased by restaurants is wasted in the kitchen before reaching the consumer. Restaurant goers, on average, leave 17 percent of their meals uneaten. These factors contribute to the staggering amount of restaurant-based food waste in the United States.

In addition to food waste in restaurants, American households discard about 25 percent of the food that they purchase. Because some foods are cheap and **abound** in grocery stores, there is sometimes a lack of emphasis on using what is purchased. Families may purchase **surplus** food, often at a discount, but not consume all that they buy. Moreover, confusion about expiration dates causes consumers to throw away food prematurely.

Any solution to the food waste problem must be comprehensive, not **piecemeal**. A national **dialogue** about food waste must **implore** people to change their habits. With heightened consumer awareness, the United States can make adjustments to production methods and consumer behavior.

Passage 2

Worldwide food production requires significant natural resources, including land and water. Not all food requires the same amount of natural resources. The production of beef and milk from cows that **bellow** on farms requires substantial amounts of water, food, and land. For example, producing just one pound of beef requires 1,800 gallons of water.

Discarding food also means discarding the natural resources used to produce that food. A recent study found that Americans wasted 23 percent of every pound of beef. That means 400 gallons of water were also wasted when that beef was tossed in the trash can. Disposing of 1.3 billion tons of food worldwide amounts to wasting 45 trillion gallons of water.

The United States landfills 30 million tons of food waste each year. Food waste accounts for 18 percent of the **clutter** in landfills. In landfills, bacteria break down food and produce methane, a greenhouse gas that is more potent than carbon dioxide. Reducing greenhouse gases is important to combat climate change.

These statistics are not intended to present a **morbid** view of the future, nor are they designed to create **turmoil** about the detrimental effects of food waste on the environment. There are some simple solutions that can produce important changes. Composting excess food creates fertilizer. Eating leftovers reduces the amount of food wasted. Everyone can play a part in reducing food waste.

1. The author of Passage 1 focuses on food waste in
   A) households and restaurants.
   B) farms and households.
   C) restaurants and stores.
   D) farms and stores.

2. As it is used in line 22, "surplus" most nearly means
   A) excellent.
   B) excess.
   C) expensive.
   D) expired.

3. As it is used in line 30, "implore" most nearly means
   A) to deter.
   B) to distract.
   C) to illustrate.
   D) to beg.

4. What is the main idea of Passage 2?
   A) Food waste contributes to the world's landfills.
   B) Food waste diminishes the world's water supply.
   C) Food waste negatively impacts the environment.
   D) Food waste creates harmful greenhouse gases.

5. As it is used in line 40, the word "bellow" most nearly means
   A) roar.
   B) graze.
   C) roam.
   D) live.

6. As it is used in line 63, the word "turmoil" most nearly means
   A) a state of anticipation.
   B) the fear of upcoming events.
   C) a state of great confusion.
   D) the fear of consequences.

7. What is the overall relationship between Passage 1 and Passage 2?
   A) Passage 1 presents the problem of food waste and Passage 2 offers solutions to this problem.
   B) Passage 1 is about the causes of food waste and Passage 2 is about the impact of food waste.
   C) Passage 1 contains statistics about food waste and Passage 2 contains stories about food waste.
   D) Passage 1 is about restaurant food waste and Passage 2 is about food waste in landfills.

8. The authors of Passage 1 and Passage 2 would most likely agree that
   A) food waste is not getting enough attention in the media.
   B) people in the United States waste more food than their counterparts worldwide.
   C) the U.S. government must find a solution to the world food waste problem.
   D) changing consumer habits can help combat the problem of food waste.

9. In Passage 1, the author states that households and restaurants contribute to the food waste problem. In Passage 2, the author argues that the food waste is significant because
   A) it wastes significant natural resources.
   B) it creates greenhouse gases.
   C) cows are kept on farms.
   D) excess food is composted.

10. Which choice provides the best evidence for the answer to the previous question?
   A) Lines 38–43 ("The production ... water")
   B) Lines 50–52 ("Disposing of ... water")
   C) Lines 56–58 ("In landfills … dioxide")
   D) Lines 67–68 ("Composting … fertilizer")

From the word bank below, choose the word that has the same or nearly the same meaning as the ***boldface*** *word in each sentence and write it on the line. You will not use all of the words.*

bellow	**infamous**	**overture**	**timidity**
despondent	**innumerable**	**piecemeal**	**turmoil**
emblem	**lax**	**random**	**veto**
hearth	**morbid**	**shirk**	**wilt**

1. The tour guide told entertaining stories about **scandalous** figures from the city's history. ______________

2. The book publisher's **symbol**, a rocket ship, appears on the spine of all its books. ______________

3. **Countless** people rely on public transportation to get to work every day. ______________

4. Don't you ever feel **depressed** after reading books and seeing movies about true crime and crime scene investigations? ______________

5. When a world championship game is being played, it's hard to blame someone for wanting to **dodge** his or her chores in order to watch the action. ______________

6. A mouse often serves as a symbol of **faintheartedness**, while a lion often represents courage. ______________

7. According to the St. Louis Zoo, a hippopotamus's **howl** can be "louder than a heavy-metal band playing 15 feet away." ______________

8. Lately I have been **remiss** about practicing my guitar chords, but I plan to start playing again tomorrow. ______________

9. Millions of fans were **dejected** when they learned that their favorite television series would come to an end next year. ______________

10. The classic sports car has been in the garage for a year and a half while the mechanic has been rebuilding its engine **bit by bit**. ______________

11. The detective was able to see that the seemingly **haphazard** series of numbers was actually a message written in code. ______________

12. Charles Dickens's *A Tale of Two Cities* is set during the **tumult** of the French Revolution. ______________

Select the pair of words that best completes the meaning of each of the following sentences.

1. As he sat by the fire that glowed in the ________________, the old sailor entertained the children with a(n) ________________ of his adventures on the high seas, beginning when he was a boy of twelve, almost sixty years before.

a. lair … farce
b. cache … dialogue
c. hearth … narrative
d. clutter … overture

2. Among law enforcement, his ________________ is that of a ________________ con artist who targets segments of the population that are likely to fall prey to his convincing words.

a. havoc … braggart
b. misdemeanor … narrative
c. dialogue … grueling
d. status … notorious

3. The earliest inhabitants of North America lived ________________ lives. They were constantly moving from place to place in search of the game that made up the greater part of their diet. This endless ________________ for food eventually took them to all parts of the continent.

a. nomadic … quest
b. grueling … cache
c. pampered … malady
d. lethargic … status

4. A communication between the warring factions' two leaders was the ________________ to a bold new peace ________________ that would end a twenty-year-long conflict.

a. beneficiary … veto
b. stalemate … status
c. overture … pact
d. surplus … farce

5. Since the soil is so remarkably rich and fertile, a variety of crops can be grown in ________________. The farmers keep what they need for themselves and sell off the ________________ at a handsome profit.

a. abundance … surplus
b. seclusion … reinforcements
c. lavishness … hospitality
d. leisure … adequacy

6. "I am still ________________ the matter over in my mind," the president told the press. "When I have reached a decision, I will either sign the bill or ________________ it."

a. mellowing … botch
b. narrating … dismantle
c. mulling … veto
d. clarifying … mar

7. Before we can even think about renovating this ________________ old house, we must remove all the worthless ________________ that is strewn around the rooms and blocking the entrances.

a. gigantic … cache
b. dilapidated … clutter
c. mellow … havoc
d. futile … surplus

Denotation and Connotation

When you look up a word in the dictionary, you get its **denotation**, or literal meaning. Many words also have **connotations**—implied meanings that we commonly associate with them.

Connotations may be positive, negative, or neutral. A word's synonyms—words that mean nearly the same thing—can have very different connotations, some more positive or more negative than others. Consider these synonyms for the neutral word *avoid*.

sidestep *evade* *shirk* *neglect*

Sidestep and *evade* have neutral to mildly negative connotations, but *shirk* and *neglect* have strongly negative connotations.

Look at these examples of words that are similar in denotation but have different connotations.

NEUTRAL	POSITIVE	NEGATIVE
difficult	**challenging**	**grueling**
slowly	**leisurely**	**slothfully**
soft	**mellow**	**slack**

Expressing the Connotation

Read each sentence. Select the word in parentheses that better expresses the connotation (positive, negative, or neutral) given at the beginning of the sentence.

neutral **1.** A mysterious (**illness, malady**) forced me to miss class that day.

positive **2.** Even after the "once in a lifetime" sales event, there was a (**surplus, glut**) of merchandise left in the furniture store.

negative **3.** Melinda goes about her chores in a(n) (**lethargic, unhurried**) way.

positive **4.** The care he received in the hospital after his accident was completely (**satisfactory, adequate**).

negative **5.** The attack from Planet X-5155 created (**havoc, disorder**) in Earth's cities.

negative **6.** Trying to find a gift he'll like is a(n) (**futile, ineffective**) exercise.

positive **7.** She was the (**recipient, beneficiary**) of the valuable knowledge passed down by her mother, a famous scholar.

neutral **8.** As a youth, Mr. Fredericks had pursued a (**vagrant, nomadic**) way of life.

Classical Roots

note, not—to know, recognize, or mark

This Latin root appears in **notorious** (page 146), which means "widely and unfavorably known." Some other words based on the same root are listed below.

connote	**notary**	**noteworthy**	**notion**
denote	**notation**	**notify**	**notoriety**

From the list of words above, choose the one that corresponds to each of the brief definitions below. Write the word in the blank space in the illustrative sentence below the definition. Use a dictionary if necessary.

1. ill fame; being famous for something bad
Jesse James achieved ____________________ as an outlaw in the Old West.

2. a record; a note to assist memory, memorandum; a set of symbols or expressions
Good students often write ____________________ in the margins of books.

3. a public official who certifies statements and signatures
The ____________________ public witnessed the signing of Grandfather's will.

4. to indicate, be the sign of, mean exactly
The child's high temperature and chills ____________________ severe illness.

5. to suggest or imply in addition to giving an exact meaning
The name *Angela* means "angel," but it also ____________________ goodness.

6. remarkable, outstanding because of some special excellence (*"worthy of being recognized"*)
The senator made ____________________ remarks about the importance of reducing air pollution.

7. to point out, give notice of, inform
We will ____________________ our attorney of your intention to sue us.

8. an idea; a foolish idea or opinion; a small useful item
She has the odd ____________________ that no one in her class likes her.

UNIT 13

*Read the following passage, taking note of the **boldface** words and their contexts. These words are among those you will be studying in Unit 13. It may help you to complete the exercises in this Unit if you refer to the way the words are used below.*

The Last Flight of the *Hindenburg*

<Radio Broadcast Transcript>

In 1936, the biggest airship (also called a dirigible or zeppelin) the world has ever seen took to the skies for the first time. The German *Hindenburg* could cross the Atlantic in just two days. It was filled with highly flammable, lighter-than-air hydrogen gas. The following transcript describes the events of May 6, 1937.

Harold Bickerson for WLEN in Springfield: *Hello, everyone. This is Harold Bickerson speaking to you from the naval airbase at Lakehurst, New Jersey, where the giant* Hindenburg *airship is about to land. While that great dirigible circles overhead, I'll recount the* **chronological** *sequence of its travels. After departing from Frankfurt, Germany, the airship spent two days speeding over miles of ocean. Though the* Hindenburg *was scheduled to land at dawn, its travel time* **fluctuates** *with wind conditions. Favorable conditions reduce the travel time, while unfavorable headwinds* **diminish** *its speed and increase travel time considerably. The ship appeared over the New York metropolitan area around noon, but the crew could not* **countenance** *a landing at that time. Shifting surface winds and air* **agitation** *at the time made landing too dangerous.*

It's just about sunset and raining fairly heavily. I'll say a few words about the preparations that have been made on the ground. The Lakehurst airbase has played a great part in the **saga** *of lighter-than-air transportation in this country, and it's well equipped to handle large hydrogen-filled airships of the* Hindenburg's **magnitude**. *The ground crew have been preparing the field. They're a* **reputable** *staff, well-known and trained to ease the giant zeppelin onto the ground. When the airship arrives, it will drop*

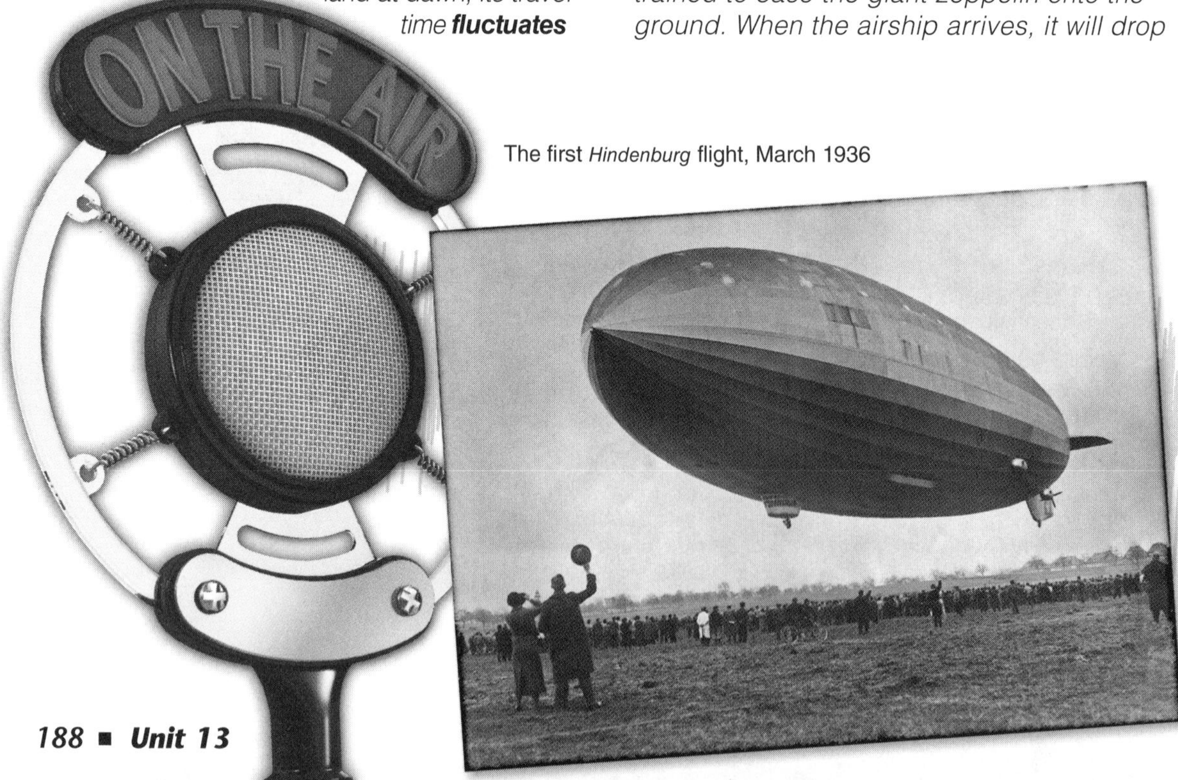

The first *Hindenburg* flight, March 1936

A Ball of Fire: The *Hindenburg* in flames after its disaster, May 6, 1937

heavy ropes to the men below, and these ropes will be affixed to the ***massive*** *mooring mast to anchor the 804-foot–long ship.*

Here comes the Hindenburg *now: It's a beautiful sight, enough to* ***enchant*** *the most sober observer and* ***foster*** *a feeling of excitement in the most jaded and* ***stodgy*** *onlooker. The* Hindenburg *is pointed directly at the mooring mast. I can see the passenger quarters and the observation deck, where the passengers must be gazing down at the great mass of humanity below them. The propellers are moving just a little to keep the ship....*

It burst into flames! It burst into flames! The Hindenburg *is burning, and it's falling, it's crashing to the ground! Watch out, watch out, folks! Oh, it's horrible, it's... The* Hindenburg *is crashing into the mooring mast, and all the people on the field are running for their lives and screaming. This is the making of a catastrophe, ladies and gentlemen. There's no chance anyone could survive this... I can't... The flames are swelling perhaps 500 feet up in the sky, and a smoky* ***pall*** *is spreading over the field, and I'm sorry, ladies and gentlemen, I can hardly breathe or talk because of the smoke. I have to move inside.*

I'm back now. The wreckage is still flaming and crackling out there. We're not sure what ***ignited*** *the ship, but something may have slipped on the craft and caused a spark, or caused the highly flammable hydrogen gas to leak. But I have some good news related to something I hurriedly* ***blurted*** *out earlier. Ambulances have arrived, and I'm told that the ground crew managed to get out of the way unharmed. And of the 97 people on board, at least 25 have been rescued. Evidently many jumped out of the windows as the ship fell to the ground. And now I'll have to pause again, because they're asking for help out there, and I must to do my part.*

Of the 97 people on board, 35 died, as did one person on the ground. The era of commercial airships was over.

Audio

For iWords and audio passages, go to **SadlierConnect.com.**

Definitions

Note the spelling, pronunciation, part(s) of speech, and definition(s) of each of the following words. Then write the appropriate form of the word in the blank space in the illustrative sentence(s) following.

1. blurt (blərt)
(*v.*) to say suddenly or without thinking
I was fairly certain that, after hours of interrogation, the suspect would ____________ out the truth.

2. countenance (kaủn′ tə nəns)
(*n.*) a face, facial expression; (*v.*) to tolerate or approve
The teacher's smiling ____________ reassured us that the rehearsal was going well.
The new boss is strict and does not ____________ lateness or absenteeism.

3. enchant (en chant′)
(*v.*) to please greatly; to charm, put under a magic spell
The singer proceeded to ____________ the audience with her beautiful voice and engaging style.

4. foster (fôs′ tər)
(*v.*) to bring up, give care to; to promote, encourage; (*adj.*) in the same family but not related by birth
The American ambassador worked to ____________ positive relations with the newly formed republic.
It is important for ____________ children to be placed with loving families.

5. handicraft (han′ dē kraft)
(*n.*) work done by hand; a trade requiring hand skill
Making apple-head dolls is a ____________ still enjoyed in the Arkansas River Valley, among other places.

6. ignite (ig nīt′)
(*v.*) to set on fire, cause to burn; to heat up, excite
We used lighter fluid to ____________ the charcoal in the outdoor grill.

7. massive (mas′ iv)
(*adj.*) large and heavy; great in size or scope
A ____________ boulder still blocks the entrance to the secret cave.

8. pall (pôl)
(*v.*) to lose in interest, attraction, or effectiveness; to become tiresome; (*n.*) a dark covering, something that conceals
When the excavation yielded only pieces of pottery, the archaeologist's optimism began to ____________.
News of the surprise attack on Pearl Harbor cast a ____________ over the nation on December 7, 1941.

9. reputable (rep′ yət ə bəl) — (*adj.*) well thought of, having a good reputation

A list of ____________________ lawyers is available through the local bar association.

10. stodgy (stäj′ ē) — (*adj.*) dull, boring; old-fashioned, hidebound; lumpy, thick

The ____________________ politician showed little inclination to listen to the speeches of junior senators.

*For each item, determine whether the **boldface** word from pages 190–191 makes sense in the context of the sentence. Circle the item numbers next to the six sentences in which the words are used correctly.*

1. Instead of putting on a **stodgy** production, the director is looking for ways to breathe new life into the classic play.

2. The spy was skilled at finding ways to **foster** the enemy and obtain important information.

3. The cook had to **countenance** the recipe in order to serve the additional guests.

4. In the fairy tale, the witch swore that she would **enchant** the guests at the party and cause them to sleep for a hundred years.

5. Weaving is a **handicraft** that dates back to prehistoric times.

6. A lightning strike can **ignite** a tree and, under certain conditions, cause a huge forest fire.

7. Tsunamis are **massive** waves that can bring great destruction when they hit land.

8. I could not **blurt** out the stains that formed on my shirt after eating a slice of pizza.

9. Sometimes the **reputable** actions of a few individuals can damage the image of an entire company.

10. Our team's loss cast a **pall** over everyone at first, but our gloominess didn't last long.

Choosing the Right Word

*Select the **boldface** word that better completes each sentence. You might refer to the passage on pages 188–189 to see how most of these words are used in context. Note that the choices might be related forms of the Unit words.*

1. For more than a hundred years, the delightful *Alice's Adventures in Wonderland* has been (**palling, enchanting**) readers young and old.

2. Her charming personality and sparkling wit brought a breath of fresh air into the (**stodgy, massive**) atmosphere of the stuffy old club.

3. My love of reading, (**fostered, blurted**) by my parents since early childhood, has continued to grow through the years.

4. One of the sure signs of a country that is not free is that the people in power will not (**countenance, blurt**) any criticism of their acts.

5. The Tea Act of 1773 was one of the sparks that helped (**enchant, ignite**) the American Revolution.

6. In my excitement, I accidentally (**blurted, ignited**) out the very thing that I was trying so hard to conceal.

7. Marta refuses to swim in the ocean as she is fearful of (**stodgy, massive**) sharks.

8. Many professionals and executives today have made enjoyable hobbies of such (**handicrafts, countenances**) as carpentry and weaving.

9. Any editorial about pollution appearing in such a (**stodgy, reputable**) newspaper is bound to make a strong impression on many citizens.

10. For a long time my favorite TV entertainment was police and detective programs, but now they are beginning to (**pall, enchant**).

11. (**Fostered, Ignited**) by the civil rights movement, the students organized several sit-ins and challenged the status quo.

12. The speaker warned that our whole system of handling lawbreakers has (**massive, stodgy**) faults that will be difficult to correct.

Completing the Sentence

Choose the word from the word bank that best completes each of the following sentences. Write the correct word or form of the word in the space provided.

blurt	enchant	handicraft	massive	reputable
countenance	foster	ignite	pall	stodgy

1. How can you ________________ such rude behavior in a young child!

2. She was very fortunate to have had talented and sympathetic teachers who ________________ her career.

3. The pilot light of the stove will automatically ________________ the burner when the handle is turned to the "on" position.

4. "When I was living in the Australian outback, I learned many curious skills and ________________ from the local people," the explorer said.

5. Statements ________________ out in anger may often be regretted for a long time afterward.

6. The audience was ________________ not only by the lovely voice of the soprano, but also by her youthful good looks.

7. We will donate the proceeds of the cake sale to any ________________ charity you may select.

8. His attitude is so incredibly ________________ and hidebound that he would have been considered old-fashioned 100 years ago!

9. All of a sudden, from out of the fog loomed a(n) ________________ ocean liner bearing down on our small boat.

10. We had hoped to have a wonderful time at the party, but the sad news of the principal's accident cast a(n) ________________ over the gathering.

End Set A

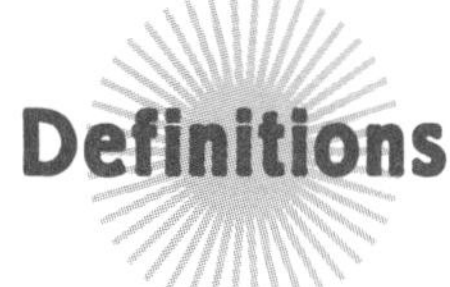

Definitions

Note the spelling, pronunciation, part(s) of speech, and definition(s) of each of the following words. Then write the appropriate form of the word in the blank space in the illustrative sentence(s) following.

1. agitation (aj i tā′ shən)
(*n.*) a violent stirring or movement; noisy confusion, excitement; a stirring up of public enthusiasm
The ____________________ for campaign finance reform was gaining widespread support in Congress.

2. chronological (krän əl äj′ i kəl)
(*adj.*) arranged in order of time of occurrence
The importance of a time line is that it arranges historical events in ____________________ order.

3. diminish (di min′ ish)
(*v.*) to make or become smaller, reduce in size
It takes no time at all for a fad to ____________________ in popularity.

4. fluctuate (flək′ chü āt)
(*v.*) to change continually; to move up and down
Stock prices ____________________ daily.

5. grovel (gräv′ əl)
(*v.*) to humble oneself, act in a fearful and servile way; to lie face downward; to indulge in something base or unworthy
Afraid of punishment, the Roman slave began to ____________________ at the feet of the emperor.

6. hilarious (hi lâr′ ē əs)
(*adj.*) extremely funny, causing loud amusement
The comedian told a ____________________ story that had the audience laughing hysterically.

7. magnitude (mag′ nə tüd)
(*n.*) the great size or importance of something
At first, the ____________________ of the task seemed to be overwhelming for a group as small as ours.

8. maternal (mə tər′ nəl)
(*adj.*) of or like a mother
The kittens' mother took her ____________________ responsibilities very seriously.

9. revere (ri vēr′) — (*v.*) to love and respect deeply, honor greatly

The elderly teacher was ______________ by a whole generation of students.

10. saga (säg′ ə) — (*n.*) a narrative of heroic exploits; a long, detailed account

Although written in Old English, *Beowulf* is very much like a Norse ______________ in that it details the colorful deeds of a legendary hero.

Using Context

For each item, determine whether the ***boldface*** *word from pages 194–195 makes sense in the context of the sentence. Circle the item numbers next to the six sentences in which the words are used correctly.*

1. I prefer to **fluctuate** among the crowd at parties, rather than doing anything to make myself stand out in front of so many people.

2. She explained that the story of how she had come to move here was too long to go over right now, but she gave me a quick **saga** with just the main facts.

3. While the book is interesting, I wish the author had told the story in **chronological** order rather than jumping back and forth between time periods.

4. Her **maternal** instincts are so strong that she can't bear to see children cry without stopping to comfort them.

5. While the medication did not make my headache go away completely, it did **diminish** the pain significantly.

6. I must not have understood all the humor in the movie, because I found it simply amusing while others thought it was completely **hilarious**.

7. The **agitation** that comes over me as soon as I reach my favorite place by the lake is enough to make me forget all of my worries and just live in the moment.

8. The chief firefighter was honored to see how many people seemed to **revere** him when they came to celebrate and honor him at his retirement party.

9. When I received my college acceptance letter, I was so shocked that the **magnitude** of what this meant for my future took a few minutes to set in.

10. When the inexperienced comedian heard the crowd **grovel** at his new jokes, he started to think he may actually one day become a famous performer.

Set B

Choosing the Right Word

*Select the **boldface** word that better completes each sentence. You might refer to the passage on pages 188–189 to see how most of these words are used in context. Note that the choices might be related forms of the Unit words.*

1. I have difficulty remembering the correct (**chronology, agitation**) of the many battles that took place during the Civil War.

2. The cowboy on his trusty quarter horse plays a prominent part in the (**magnitude, saga**) of the Old West.

3. She kept us in stitches with her (**chronological, hilarious**) jokes.

4. Though there has of late been a good deal of (**magnitude, agitation**) for tax reform, nothing much has come of it so far.

5. I'm writing a (**saga, magnitude**) that depicts one courageous soldier's devotion to the cause of freedom during the Civil War.

6. As the game proceeded, and the ball continued to change hands, our feelings (**revered, fluctuated**) from joy to despair and back again.

7. The movie was difficult to follow because its many short scenes did not follow a traditional (**chronological, maternal**) order.

8. If it were not for the strong (**maternal, hilarious**) instinct to protect their young, many species of animals could not survive.

9. Rather than (**diminish, grovel**) in your self-pity and play the role of the victim, why don't you take a stand and confront your accuser.

10. Many older people complain that the warm spirit of neighborliness has greatly (**diminished, revered**) under the conditions of city living.

11. Some controversial figures are both (**revered, fluctuated**) as saints and despised as villians.

12. When the Wright brothers made the first successful airplane flight, few people realized the (**saga, magnitude**) of their achievement.

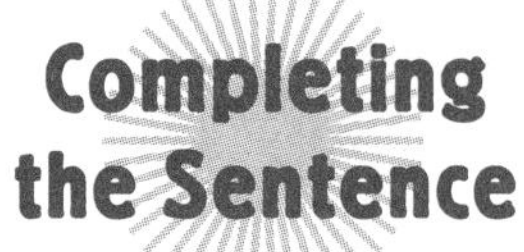

Completing the Sentence

Choose the word from the word bank that best completes each of the following sentences. Write the correct word or form of the word in the space provided.

agitation	**diminish**	**grovel**	**magnitude**	**revere**
chronological	**fluctuate**	**hilarious**	**maternal**	**saga**

1. With no money coming in and my daily expenses continuing to mount, my savings have ____________________ at an alarming rate.

2. The number and the ____________________ of the problems faced by the President of the United States are almost beyond our imagination.

3. The two little girls playing house fussed over their dolls with all the ____________________ attention that their own mothers bestowed on them.

4. Can you imagine my ____________________ when I was told I would have to take over the lead role in the play immediately, with no rehearsals!

5. Instead of moving steadily upward or steadily downward, the price of oil has been ____________________ all year.

6. The waves of laughter from the audience indicated that those around me found the clown's antics as ____________________ as I did.

7. Educators report that there is often a vast difference between a child's mental age and his or her ____________________ age.

8. In the ____________________ *of Eric the Red*, there is a very interesting account of the Norse discovery of North America in 1000 CE.

9. Even though I need a job badly, I still have my self-respect, and I am not going to ____________________ just to get work.

10. Our study of American history has taught us to ____________________ the great men and women who founded this nation.

End Set B

Synonyms

*Choose the word or form of the word from this Unit that is the same or most nearly the same in meaning as the **boldface** word or expression in the phrase. Write that word on the line. Use a dictionary if necessary.*

1. will **accept** the president's proposal ______
2. the **enormity** of an earthquake ______
3. signs of **uneasiness** on his face ______
4. **captivated** by the princess's beauty ______
5. will **cower** before the king ______
6. interest in dolls **dwindles** with age ______
7. a somber and **stuffy** old man ______
8. attempted to **nurture** positive relations ______
9. trust only in **reliable** information ______
10. listed in **consecutive** order ______
11. an **heroic tale** in ancient Greek ______
12. **inflamed** the tense situation ______
13. temperatures that **vary** wildly ______
14. to **reveal** the truth ______
15. launched a **monumental** attack ______

Antonyms

*Choose the word or form of the word from this Unit that is most nearly opposite in meaning to the **boldface** word or expression in the phrase. Write that word on the line. Use a dictionary if necessary.*

1. **increase** in strength ______
2. known for their **machine-made products** ______
3. inheriting a **fatherly** trait ______
4. a meeting to address a **serious** matter ______
5. to **deride** the Romantic poets ______

Writing: Words in Action

Think about how air travel has changed since the flight of the *Hindenburg*. Do you think air travel is safer today than it was in 1936? Write a persuasive essay in which you support your opinion. Use at least two details from the passage (pages 188–189) and three or more words from this Unit.

Vocabulary in Context

*Some of the words you have studied in this Unit appear in **boldface** type. Read the passage below, and then circle the letter of the correct answer for each word as it is used in context.*

On August 17, 2016, the *Airlander 10*, a helium-filled airship, flew over central England. With its bulbous front end, the largest aircraft currently flying may have looked **hilarious**. In reality, observers were witnessing an amazing feat of **handicraft** and technical innovation in action.

The *Airlander 10* is a blimp-shaped helium-filled airship. It is 302 feet long and can carry 10 metric tons while reaching heights of 16,000 feet. In addition, it can travel at speeds up to 90 miles per hour. It is a hybrid of a blimp, a helicopter, and an airplane, and it can stay in the air for two weeks at a time. The helium inside the *Airlander 10* is not flammable; therefore, it will not **ignite** like the *Hindenburg* did in 1937.

The *Airlander 10* was originally designed for U.S. military surveillance, but in 2013, the U.S. military eliminated its blimp program. The company that created the *Airlander 10* had to ask for funding from individuals and government agencies. The company did not get so desperate as to **grovel** for money, however, because it was awarded several lucrative grants from the United Kingdom and the European Union.

Because it uses less fuel than a plane, the *Airlander 10* is a more environmentally friendly type of air travel. At a ceremony in April 2016, it was rechristened the *Martha Gwyn*—an aptly **maternal** name for a vehicle that promises to protect the environment. Though some critics are skeptical about whether this hybrid airship will become commercially successful, others **revere** the science behind the impressive machine.

---

1. What is the meaning of **hilarious** as it is used in paragraph 1?

a. interesting
b. complicated
c. dangerous
d. funny

2. The word **handicraft** means about the same as

a. work done by hand
b. work requiring skill
c. work done quickly
d. work needing repair

3. **Ignite** comes from the Latin word **ignis**. **Ignis** most likely means

a. roar
b. fire
c. chaos
d. destruction

4. What is the meaning of **grovel** as it is used in paragraph 3?

a. to request a sum
b. to make a speech
c. to humble oneself
d. to act falsely

5. Which word means the same as **maternal** as it is used in paragraph 4?

a. protective
b. indifferent
c. beautiful
d. difficult

6. What does the word **revere** most likely mean as it is used in paragraph 4?

a. doubt
b. respect
c. study
d. observe

UNIT 14

*Read the following passage, taking note of the **boldface** words and their contexts. These words are among those you will be studying in Unit 14. It may help you to complete the exercises in this Unit if you refer to the way the words are used below.*

Celebrating the Death of a Killer

<Online Article>

by Aisha B. Boulos

GENEVA, SWITZERLAND The year 2012 marks the thirty-fifth anniversary of the last naturally occurring case of the highly contagious smallpox virus on the planet. The victim of the disfiguring and sometimes deadly **affliction** was a young man in the East African country of Somalia. Fortunately, after prompt treatment, the patient survived this deadly disease that has plagued humanity for centuries.

Two and a half years later, at a **gala** celebration at its headquarters in Geneva, Switzerland, the World Health Organization (WHO) officially declared that the disease had finally been eradicated. The history of smallpox stretches back over 3,500 years. The peoples of the world owe a debt of **gratitude** to WHO.

How did a single agency of the United Nations, with very little money and only a limited, **meager** staff, **vanquish** this killer disease in only a decade (1967–1977)? The story of the eradication of smallpox might seem like a **hoax**, if it were not for the fact that it is entirely true. It is a tale of persistence, determination, and the imaginative handling of stiff challenges.

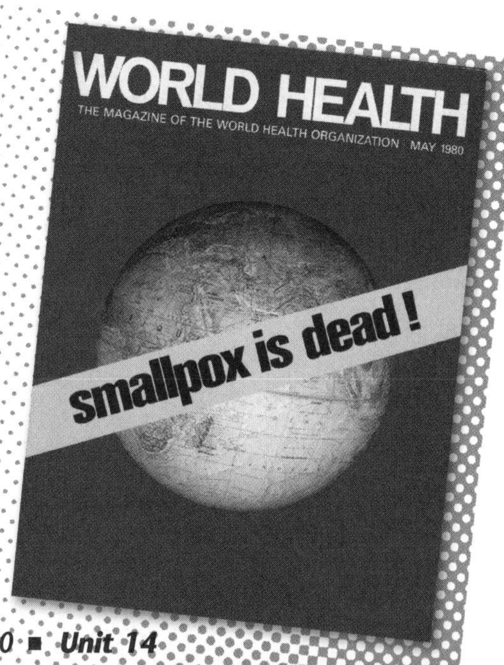

WORLD HEALTH
THE MAGAZINE OF THE WORLD HEALTH ORGANIZATION · MAY 1980
smallpox is dead!

In 1959, smallpox was present in 59 countries, all of them located in Latin America, Asia, and Africa. Experts have estimated that there were about 10 million new cases annually. Approximately one third were fatal. In the previous century, the smallpox virus had caused the deaths of at least half a billion people. This staggering total may be compared with the roughly 150 million deaths caused by warfare during the same period. For many of those **meditating** a global attack on smallpox, their intentions and hopes must have seemed **wan** and weak indeed. No other disease had ever been eradicated worldwide before. Even the director-general of WHO suggested that such an **inflated** goal might lie beyond the pale.

Nevertheless, the WHO team, refusing to **heed** conventional wisdom, sallied forth in January 1967. It was led by the American epidemiologist D.A. Henderson. His study of smallpox and its characteristics convinced Henderson that the team could meet the challenge. First, the virus infected only humans, so there was no reservoir in nature. Each infected person exhibited a telltale rash. If victims were isolated immediately, they could be prevented from **transmitting** the virus to others. Perhaps most critical of all, experts had developed a stable, inexpensive, freeze-dried vaccine against smallpox. A single vaccination provided immunity for at least ten years.

Despite these advantages, however, the WHO team had to confront formidable obstacles. Besides the skepticism of senior officials,

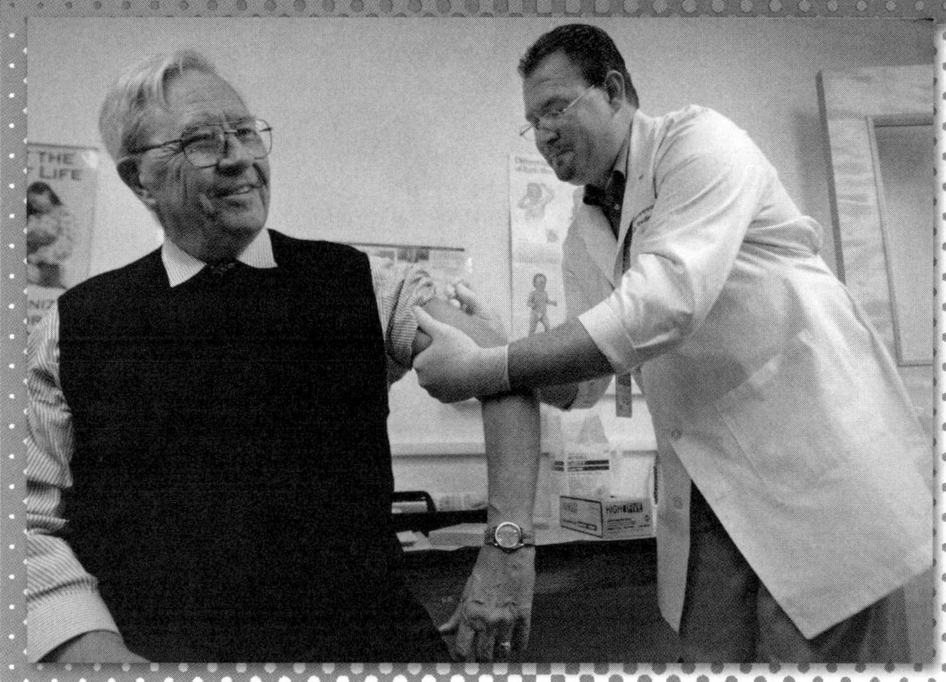

Dr. Henderson, leader of the WHO team against smallpox, receives his smallpox vaccine.

the WHO staff members had to deal with roads in terrible disrepair, broken-down vehicles, war zones, and cultural opposition to vaccination. There were also geographical barriers. Large mountainous areas of Ethiopia, for instance, were inaccessible except for **pedestrians** or for travelers on mule-back. Communications were an ongoing problem. Drought, famine, and tides of refugees **oppressed** the team's efforts in some areas.

Yet somehow the team got it done. By 1980, a **cosmopolitan** and **impartial** killer with billions of victims around the world, including emperors and monarchs, was gone. Ramses V of Egypt, Joseph I of Austria, Louis XV of France: All their wealth and power did little to **elongate** their lives once they contracted smallpox. A small but intrepid team from WHO turned out to be the disease's most potent adversary.

This article appeared in section B, page B5, of the January 4, 2012, print edition of the Times.

WHO kept meticulous track of which areas were still being infected by smallpox.

Audio

For iWords and audio passages, go to **SadlierConnect.com**.

Note the spelling, pronunciation, part(s) of speech, and definition(s) of each of the following words. Then write the appropriate form of the word in the blank space in the illustrative sentence(s) following.

1. akin (ə kin′)
(*adj.*) related by blood; having similar qualities or character
Our neighbors seem to have ideas ____________________ to ours about landscaping.

2. elongate (i lôŋ′ gāt)
(*v.*) to grow in length, become longer; to extend the length of
The artist sought to ____________________ the trunk of the elephant in her caricature in order to amuse the children.

3. gaudy (gô′ dē)
(*adj.*) flashy, showy; not in good taste
The singer's ____________________ outfit was totally inappropriate for a command performance before the queen.

4. gratitude (grat′ ə tüd)
(*n.*) appreciation, thankfulness
Be sure to express your ____________________ to your teacher for having written you a letter of recommendation.

5. hoax (hōks)
(*n.*) an act intended to trick or deceive, a fraud;
(*v.*) to trick, deceive
Their plan was to ____________________ people into believing that they had found a masterpiece.

6. impostor (im päs′ tər)
(*n.*) a swindler, deceiver; one who uses a false name or character in order to cheat
After having posed as a doctor for five years, the man was finally exposed as an ____________________.

7. meditate (med′ ə tāt)
(*v.*) to think about deeply and quietly, reflect upon; to plan, intend
Many ancient philosophers would seek peaceful surroundings in which to ____________________ on the meaning of life.

8. nutritious (nü trish′ əs)
(*adj.*) nourishing; valuable and satisfying as food
My mother cooks ____________________ meals to ensure that we have a balanced diet.

9. pedestrian (pə des′ trē ən)
(*n.*) one who goes on foot; (*adj.*) relating to walking; on foot; ordinary, unimaginative

The driver slammed on the brakes and swerved so as not to hit the ____________________.

Critics denounced his ____________________ literary style, but his book sales were high.

10. transmit (tranz mit′)
(*v.*) to send on, pass along, send out

In the Old West, local sheriffs would ____________________ messages by telegraph to the marshal of the territory.

Using Context

*For each item, determine whether the **boldface** word from pages 202–203 makes sense in the context of the sentence. Circle the item numbers next to the six sentences in which the words are used correctly.*

1. The inscription on the World War I memorial expressed eternal **gratitude** for the sacrifices made by soldiers who had served and died.
2. The apartment building is in a very convenient location; it is **akin** to the train station and within walking distance of the shops and businesses on Main Street.
3. The **impostor** not only made an effort to dress like the movie star he so closely resembled, but he also studied the actor's handwriting so that he could forge autographs.
4. Every year the children's hospital organizes an awards dinner to **elongate** the important contributions that many different volunteers have made.
5. No rain fell, but the sky was gray and **gaudy** all day.
6. The photo of the unicorn standing amid a herd of wild horses was proven to be a **hoax**.
7. In the modern world, it can be hard to find time to **meditate** on life's problems or to simply relax and put them aside for a little while.
8. The critic complained that although the subject of the biography was fascinating, the writing was dull and **pedestrian**.
9. The shop windows along the city's most **nutritious** street were filled with luxury items, including jewelry, handbags, and chocolates.
10. Since the 1960s, satellites in space have helped to **transmit** television signals.

Set A

Choosing the Right Word

*Select the **boldface** word that better completes each sentence. You might refer to the passage on pages 200–201 to see how most of these words are used in context. Note that the choices might be related forms of the Unit words.*

1. Try as he might, the sideshow barker couldn't convince me that the "real live mermaid" inside the tent wasn't just a clever (**hoax, pedestrian**).

2. Shakespeare's advice about dressing—"rich, not (**gaudy, akin**)"—still holds true in today's sophisticated world.

3. Is it necessary for you to go into the woods to (**elongate, meditate**) every time you have to make a routine decision?

4. In order to express my (**hoax, gratitude**) for all the help Mrs. Schroeder had given me, I made a donation to her favorite charity.

5. We are so accustomed to television that we tend to forget what a marvel it is to (**meditate, transmit**) colored images from one place to another.

6. Mere words cannot express our (**impostor, gratitude**) for your splendid services to our school.

7. He claimed to be a famous multimillionaire, but when he tried to borrow bus fare, we realized he was a(n) (**pedestrian, impostor**).

8. A viewing diet made up entirely of game shows may be entertaining, but it is not particularly (**gaudy, nutritious**), mentally speaking.

9. The spokesperson had important things to say, but his way of expressing himself was so unimaginative and (**nutritious, pedestrian**) that he lost our interest.

10. Have you ever noticed that as the sun sinks lower in the sky, shadows become (**elongated, nutritious**)?

11. Regardless of whether the light is green, (**impostors, pedestrians**) always have the right of way, according to the law.

12. I'd describe nostalgia as a feeling more (**gaudy, akin**) to yearning than to grief.

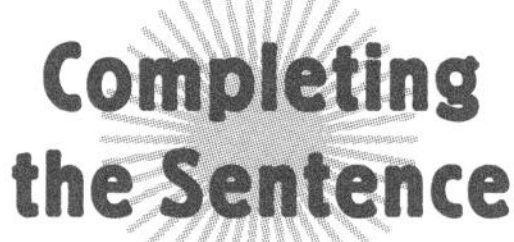

Completing the Sentence

Choose the word from the word bank that best completes each of the following sentences. Write the correct word or form of the word in the space provided.

akin	**gaudy**	**hoax**	**meditate**	**pedestrian**
elongate	**gratitude**	**impostor**	**nutritious**	**transmit**

1. Although the newspapers hailed the find as the "discovery of the century," it turned out to be nothing but an outrageous ________________.

2. Most of us are so busy with everyday concerns that we can find little or no time to ________________ on the larger issues of life.

3. An earthworm moves by first ________________ and then contracting its wonderfully elastic body.

4. The big clown's ________________ costume was in sharp contrast to the simple white outfits worn by the trapeze artists.

5. The family lawyer proved that the young man claiming to be the missing heir was no more than a(n) ________________.

6. "Although these two words are not related etymologically," the professor observed, "they are ________________ to each other in meaning."

7. I don't expect you to throw yourself on your knees, but I wish you'd show a little ________________ for the things I've done for you.

8. Junk food may look attractive and taste great, but it is by no means as ________________ as much plainer fare.

9. Most cities have now passed laws to discourage ________________ from crossing against the light or jaywalking.

10. Modern technology has provided us with the computer, a device for collecting, sorting, and ________________ information quickly.

End Set A

Definitions

Note the spelling, pronunciation, part(s) of speech, and definition(s) of each of the following words. Then write the appropriate form of the word in the blank space in the illustrative sentence(s) following.

1. affliction (ə flik′ shən)

(*n.*) a physical ailment; a cause of pain or trouble, misfortune

Lupus is a dreadful __________ suffered by nearly five million people, mostly women, worldwide.

2. cosmopolitan (käz mə päl′ ə tən)

(*adj.*) found in most parts of the world; having many fields of interest; of worldwide scope; sophisticated

It does not surprise us that our cousin, a big-city dweller, has a __________ outlook.

3. gala (gā′ lə)

(*n.*) a public entertainment marking a special event, a festive occasion; (*adj.*) festive, showy

The inexperienced reporter had never seen such finery as was worn at the __________.

The President and the First Lady attended a __________ performance at the Kennedy Center in Washington, D.C.

4. heed (hēd)

(*v.*) to pay careful attention to, notice; to be guided by; (*n.*) close attention or consideration

My parents are always telling me to __________ their advice.

Pay no __________ to old superstitions.

5. impartial (im pär′ shəl)

(*adj.*) just, unbiased, fair, not taking sides

The defense attorney knew it would be difficult to find __________ jurors to serve on the civil case.

6. inflate (in flāt′)

(*v.*) to fill with air or gas; to swell or puff out; to make something appear larger than it is

On the evening before the big parade, we watched the workers __________ the huge balloons.

7. meager (mē′ gər)

(*adj.*) poor, scant, unsatisfactory; thin, slight

He was famished by noon because he ate such a __________ breakfast.

8. oppress (ə pres′)

(*v.*) to govern or rule cruelly or unjustly; to weigh heavily upon

Too many dictators have used their absolute power to __________ the people they govern.

9. vanquish (vaŋ′ kwish) — (*v.*) to defeat in a battle or contest, overthrow; to overcome a feeling or condition

The general's goal was to ____________ his country's enemies.

10. wan (wän) — (*adj.*) unnaturally pale or sickly looking; lacking vitality; dim, faint; weak, ineffectual

The patient was so weak that all she could give the nurse was a ____________ smile.

Using Context

*For each item, determine whether the **boldface** word from pages 206–207 makes sense in the context of the sentence. Circle the item numbers next to the six sentences in which the words are used correctly.*

1. I was excited that I had made the guest list of the **gala** celebration until I realized that I had nothing nearly fancy enough to wear.

2. I tried for a long time to **inflate** the air mattress before realizing that it had a hole in it and would only keep losing air.

3. If you refuse to **heed** the advice of those more experienced than you, don't be surprised when things don't go your way.

4. I had to roll my eyes when my friend yawned and told me she was suffering from the **affliction** of being "too well-rested."

5. A screen will separate the auditioning performers from the panel of judges so that the decision-makers can remain **impartial**.

6. Our neighbors moved out so suddenly that some say they appeared to **vanquish** overnight.

7. Whenever he is down, my brother remembers this **wan** expression to cheer himself up: "Every cloud has a silver lining."

8. When I entered the large library, I was shocked at the **meager** amount of books on the shelves and doubted whether I could indeed read every one, as I had boasted.

9. Due to the elegant exterior of the house, I was surprised to find the interior decorated in such a **cosmopolitan** way, with mismatched furniture and bare walls.

10. Anxiety about all my responsibilities in the coming week continued to **oppress** my thoughts so much that I was unable to enjoy my weekend.

Choosing the Right Word

*Select the **boldface** word that better completes each sentence. You might refer to the passage on pages 200–201 to see how most of these words are used in context. Note that the choices might be related forms of the Unit words.*

1. After a lifetime of travel in dozens of countries all over the world, she is highly (**cosmopolitan, wan**) in her tastes and ideas.

2. We won the game because we kept our heads and paid no (**affliction, heed**) to the insulting remarks made by our opponents.

3. By continuing to praise his extremely modest accomplishments, you are helping to (**inflate, vanquish**) his already oversized ego.

4. Such extravaganzas as the "Night of 100 Stars" are usually designed to be (**wan, gala**) charity benefits for worthy causes.

5. Had you (**heeded, vanquished**) my advice, you would be finished by now.

6. The glowing review of my performance must be accurate, as critics do their best to be (**impartial, oppressive**) in their reviews.

7. The speaker was greeted by a(n) (**meager, impartial**) round of applause,but before she left the stage, she had the audience cheering.

8. Education and compassion are the only weapons by which we will (**heed, vanquish**) prejudice and superstition once and for all.

9. Is there any country in the world in which the terrible (**affliction, heed**) of poverty has been entirely overcome?

10. My mind and body were so (**oppressed, heeded**) by the stifling heat that afternoon that I couldn't do anything at all.

11. The man's pathetically (**wan, gala**) personality is matched only by the hopelessly bland and lifeless statements that issue from his mouth.

12. Each scholarship candidate was identified by a number so that the people doing the grading would be absolutely (**impartial, cosmopolitan**).

Completing the Sentence

Choose the word from the word bank that best completes each of the following sentences. Write the correct word or form of the word in the space provided.

affliction	**gala**	**impartial**	**meager**	**vanquish**
cosmopolitan	**heed**	**inflate**	**oppress**	**wan**

1. Because I am a very close friend of his, you cannot expect me to be totally ____________________ in judging your criticisms of him.

2. With a population made up of people from many different lands, New York City is one of the most ____________________ places in the world.

3. If you had only ____________________ my warnings, all this trouble could easily have been avoided.

4. Superstars and other celebrities are usually very much in attendance at ____________________ events, such as the opening night of a new Broadway show.

5. Unfortunately, the region cannot support a very large population because its natural resources are so ____________________.

6. The distraught mother's ____________________ expression reflected her sense of anxiety over her lost child.

7. After beating off the enemy's initial assault, our brave troops delivered a series of crippling counterattacks that ____________________ the foe.

8. Have you ever tried to ____________________ a bicycle tire with one of those old-fashioned hand pumps?

9. Modern medical science can do wonders for people suffering from various physical or emotional ____________________.

10. Refusing to be ____________________ by unjust laws, the American colonists rose in revolt against the British government.

End Set B

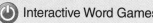

Synonyms

*Choose the word or form of the word from this Unit that is the same or most nearly the same in meaning as the **boldface** word or expression in the phrase. Write that word on the line. Use a dictionary if necessary.*

1. attended a **dull** series of lectures _______________
2. had light hair and a **pallid** complexion _______________
3. needed rest due to a serious **illness** _______________
4. would **muse** on the meaning of the universe _______________
5. **stretches** the elastic so it wraps around the bundle _______________
6. had an **exaggerated** sense of her importance _______________
7. overwhelmed by feelings of **gratefulness** _______________
8. not the message she wished to **convey** _______________
9. must **listen to** the warning _______________
10. looked glamorous for the President's **extravaganza** _______________
11. wished to remain **neutral** _______________
12. ate a **healthful** meal before the game _______________
13. tricked by the thief's **deception** _______________
14. will **subdue** all foes of the realm _______________
15. a **loud** print with red, purple, and orange flowers _______________

Antonyms

*Choose the word or form of the word from this Unit that is most nearly opposite in meaning to the **boldface** word or expression in the phrase. Write that word on the line. Use a dictionary if necessary.*

1. an **abundant** food supply _______________
2. was **dissimilar** to the views she held _______________
3. encountered an **honest person** _______________
4. had **unsophisticated** taste _______________
5. **liberated** by the incoming government _______________

Writing: Words in Action

Suppose that you work for Dr. Henderson. You want to persuade others to join the WHO team, travel to different countries, and assist with vaccinations. Write a persuasive editorial stating why this venture is a worthy cause. Use at least two details from the passage (pages 200–201) and three or more words from this Unit.

Vocabulary in Context

Some of the words you have studied in this Unit appear in ***boldface*** *type. Read the passage below, and then circle the letter of the correct answer for each word as it is used in context.*

In the early 1700s, smallpox was still one of the world's most feared diseases. Virtually everyone who supported inoculation against smallpox—or variolation, as it was then known—was regarded as an **impostor.** The supposed benefits of the smallpox vaccine were considered a **hoax.** Despite his **gaudy** credentials as an influential minister and the son of a Harvard College president, Cotton Mather, who favored inoculation, was ignored. As late as 1768, the first edition of the *Encyclopedia Britannica* still recommended bloodletting, enemas, and induced vomiting to combat the disease.

In colonial New England, there were many myths about smallpox. Could it be caused, for example, by a lack of **nutritious** food? Most people did not know that smallpox was an infectious virus.

In 1721, with a smallpox outbreak in Boston, the city was divided over the merits of inoculation. James Franklin, the young editor of the *New-England Courant* and elder brother of Benjamin, severely criticized Cotton Mather. Yet the numbers supported the inoculation advocates. There were 844 deaths in 5,889 cases of smallpox: a rate of 14 percent. The death rate of those who were inoculated was 2.4 percent.

Years later, in 1759, Benjamin Franklin was forced to admit that his efforts in favor of vaccination had been **meager,** despite the tragic loss of one of his children to smallpox in 1736. Franklin recognized that the thinking of a British doctor, William Heberden, was **akin** to his own. Together, they published a pamphlet supporting inoculation.

---

1. What is the meaning of **impostor** as it is used in paragraph 1?

a. criminal
b. deceiver
c. prophet
d. salesperson

2. In paragraph 1, what does **hoax** suggest about the vaccine's supposed benefits?

a. They are deceptive.
b. They are valid.
c. They are a convenience.
d. They are beneficial.

3. The word **gaudy** means about the same as

a. inferior
b. temporary
c. false
d. flashy

4. Which word means the same as **nutritious** as it is used in paragraph 2?

a. imported
b. fattening
c. wholesome
d. spicy

5. **Meager** comes from the Latin word **macer. Macer** most likely means

a. thin
b. ample
c. plain
d. productive

6. What does the word **akin** most likely mean as it is used in paragraph 4?

a. opposed
b. similar
c. unrelated
d. superior

*Read the following passage, taking note of the **boldface** words and their contexts. These words are among those you will be studying in Unit 15. It may help you to complete the exercises in this Unit if you refer to the way the words are used below.*

A Brief History of Gold

<Informational Essay>

Has there ever been a more precious commodity than gold? One of the rarest metals in the world, gold has been treasured, **hoarded**, sought after, and **feuded** over. It was highly prized long before the concept of exchanging money began. A ruler's wealth and power **coincided** with how much gold he had: More gold equaled more power. Even now, some view owning gold as the ultimate in financial security.

Recent scientific research suggests that gold and other metals were transported to the earth's surface by meteors billions of years ago (though there is not yet **authoritative** evidence to confirm this theory). Gold is found in the form of dust, grains, flakes, or nuggets. Surprisingly, gold is also found in seawater. Extracting it from water is expensive. Entrepreneurs attempting to recover gold from the sea would likely go **bankrupt**.

The mining of gold began many thousands of years ago. Some of the oldest gold artifacts have been unearthed in the Varna Necropolis. This ancient burial site is near Varna, Bulgaria. It contained an astounding cache of treasures.

Prospectors rest by a sluice box in California during the gold rush.

Solid gold Thracian king's mask from the 5th century BCE

Skilled goldsmiths of that era hammered gold into exquisite pieces, including solid-gold masks, goblets, and jewelry.

The world's oldest-known geological map, the Turin papyrus map (created circa 1150 BCE or Before the Common Era), indicates where the early Egyptians excavated their gold mines. Egyptians were so enamored of gold that they believed it to be a physical manifestation of the sun and the "flesh of the gods." Their pharaohs' coffins were made out of solid gold. Because of its beauty and indestructible nature, it was valued by numerous other early civilizations, from the ancient Mediterranean civilizations of the Minoans and Etruscans to the ancient American Aztecs and Incas. Gold was also used in religious **rites**. The **legacy** of age-old folk and fairy tales from around the world is full of wishes and dreams for gold.

But how did gold change from an object of beauty and worship to a **legitimate**, official form of currency? Early on, people used the barter system to get most goods and services they needed. When **haggling** proved less than **harmonious**, people moved on to primitive forms of payment such as shells, stones, beads, and fur. This system evolved over time, and many societies switched to using pieces of gold. The pieces were marked with weight and then turned into coins. The first gold coins were minted around 640 BCE in the ancient Roman province of Lydia. The Greeks also used gold coins. Goldsmith Ephraim Brasher created the first United States gold coin in 1784.

Man's greed for gold inspired European explorations and violent conquests in Central and South America. **Despots** and tyrants on all sides had "gold fever," **clamoring** loudly for more and more riches. Fortunes were quickly made, and even more quickly lost.

The discovery of gold around the world led to gold rushes, including the famous California gold rush of the 1840s. The wild outpost of Sutter's Mill attracted more than 40,000 **hardy** prospectors. Few found the mother lode. Those who did were **indisposed** to share it. Many failed prospectors returned home **cynical**, sadder, and wiser, no doubt appreciating the saying, "Better an ounce of happiness than a pound of gold."

Audio

For iWords and audio passages, go to **SadlierConnect.com.**

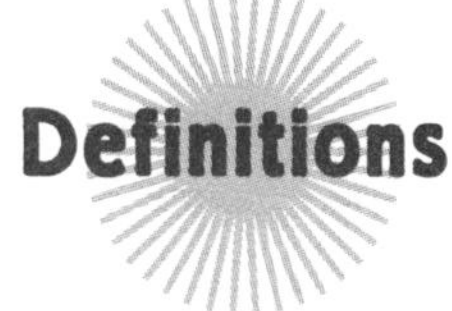

Note the spelling, pronunciation, part(s) of speech, and definition(s) of each of the following words. Then write the appropriate form of the word in the blank space in the illustrative sentence(s) following.

1. **authoritative** (ə thär′ ə tā tiv)	(*adj.*) official, coming from a source that calls for obedience or belief; dictatorial A dictionary is an ____________ source for the spelling, pronunciation, and definition of words in a language.
2. **clamor** (klam′ ər)	(*n.*) a public outcry; any loud and continued noise; (*v.*) to call for by loud, continued outcries The coal miners began to ____________ for better working conditions in the mine. The ____________ of the trumpets was piercing.
3. **feud** (fyüd)	(*n.*) a bitter, long-term quarrel; (*v.*) to fight or quarrel with A senseless ____________ caused the division between the two clans. What originally caused the clans to ____________ has long been forgotten.
4. **hardy** (här′ dē)	(*adj.*) able to bear up under difficult conditions or harsh treatment; brave and tough The saguaro is a ____________ variety of the cactus family.
5. **hoard** (hôrd)	(*v.*) to store up, save; (*n.*) a hidden store or supply Where did the miser keep his ____________ of money?
6. **indisposed** (in dis pōzd′)	(*adj., part.*) slightly ill; disinclined to do something My sister was ____________ with a bad head cold.
7. **legitimate** (lə jit′ ə mət)	(*adj.*) lawful, rightful; reasonable, justifiable There is a new committee that rules on whether complaints are ____________.
8. **mirth** (mərth)	(*n.*) merry fun, gaiety; laughter The children were filled with ____________ as they exited the Fun House.

9. officiate (ə fish′ ē āt)
(*v.*) to perform the duties of an office; to conduct a religious ceremony; to referee
Will a judge ____________________ at the ceremony?

10. sagacious (sə gā′ shəs)
(*adj.*) shrewd; wise in a keen, practical way
History has shown that ____________________ leaders exercise tolerance and fairness, along with good judgment.

Using Context

For each item, determine whether the ***boldface*** *word from pages 214–215 makes sense in the context of the sentence. Circle the item numbers next to the six sentences in which the words are used correctly.*

1. In the middle of the concert, the singer brought on a very famous surprise guest and the two sang a **feud** together.
2. The notion that planet Earth is flat was **indisposed** a long time ago.
3. The art collector was able to produce evidence to show that he was the **legitimate** owner of the valuable painting.
4. It is not enough to be generally fit and **hardy** if you want to run a marathon; you also have to spend months training and preparing for the ordeal.
5. The reporter's article is based on **authoritative** sources, such as public documents and videotaped firsthand interviews.
6. I heard a **clamor** in the kitchen and then saw that a rack holding pots and pans had come loose and fallen off the wall.
7. Older people can often give **sagacious** advice, based on lessons they have learned from experience.
8. Dogs growl and show their teeth in order to **hoard** people or animals that they find threatening.
9. The famous author had to overcome a great deal of **mirth** in order to achieve the success that she has today.
10. Does the leader of the host country **officiate** at the opening ceremonies of the Olympics?

Choosing the Right Word

*Select the **boldface** word that better completes each sentence. You might refer to the passage on pages 212–213 to see how most of these words are used in context. Note that the choices might be related forms of the Unit words.*

1. During the winter, there are always a few (**hardy, sagacious**) souls who take a dip in the icy waters off Atlantic Beach.

2. The (**indisposed, authoritative**) tone in which she gave the order left no doubt in anyone's mind that she expected full obedience.

3. We cannot accept the idea that capital and labor must constantly (**feud, hoard**) with each other.

4. She may give the impression of being simple and uncomplicated, but we have found her to be unusually (**sagacious, indisposed**) in judging people.

5. In the period ahead, there may be shortages of some foodstuffs, but we will only make things worse if we resort to (**officiating, hoarding**).

6. A good sports official pays no attention to the (**clamor, mirth**) of the crowd when a decision goes against the home team.

7. If you're looking for a witty, charming personality to (**officiate, feud**) at the awards dinner, need I say that I'm available?

8. The (**clamor, feud**) that the two sides of the family have been waging for years is about whether chili should be made with beans.

9. In the winter, Alice grows kale, as it is such a (**hardy, sagacious**) vegetable.

10. We will give careful attention to (**sagacious, legitimate**) complaints, but we will not be influenced by silly faultfinding.

11. Life cannot be all happiness; we must expect tears as well as (**clamor, mirth**).

12. I was (**hardy, indisposed**) to accept the halfhearted invitation that reached me only a day before the party.

Choose the word from the word bank that best completes each of the following sentences. Write the correct word or form of the word in the space provided.

authoritative	**feud**	**hoard**	**legitimate**	**officiate**
clamor	**hardy**	**indisposed**	**mirth**	**sagacious**

1. The referee who ____________________ at a hockey game needs the stamina to keep up with the players and the patience to put up with them.

2. Is it true that squirrels ____________________ nuts and other foods that they can use during the winter?

3. My aunt called to say that she would not be able to visit us today because she was ____________________ with an asthma attack.

4. The pioneers who settled the West were ____________________ people who could cope with difficulties and dangers of all kinds.

5. Where can I get a(n) ____________________ estimate of how the population of the United States is likely to change in the years ahead?

6. The fact that the baseball season is opening today is certainly not a(n) ____________________ excuse for being absent from school.

7. Although she had no previous experience as a treasurer, she showed herself to be highly ____________________ in the way she handled money.

8. I like a good laugh as much as anyone, but I realized that such a solemn ceremony was not the time for ____________________.

9. About five minutes before feeding time, all the babies in the nursery start to ____________________ for their bottles.

10. Historians are still examining the deadly ____________________ that arose between the Hatfield and McCoy families more than 100 years ago.

End Set A

Definitions

Note the spelling, pronunciation, part(s) of speech, and definition(s) of each of the following words. Then write the appropriate form of the word in the blank space in the illustrative sentence(s) following.

1. bankrupt (baŋk′ rəpt)

(*adj.*) in a state of financial ruin; (*v.*) to ruin financially; (*n.*) one who has been ruined financially

The ____________________ company was closing its doors for the last time.

Another bad sales year will ____________________ the firm.

A ____________________ will have trouble getting credit.

2. coincide (kō in sīd′)

(*v.*) to be in full agreement; to be the same in nature, character, or function; to happen at the same time

Our political beliefs would ____________________ with theirs on the issues of term limits and tax reform.

3. cynical (sin′ ə kəl)

(*adj.*) inclined to believe the worst of people; bitterly mocking or sneering

The radio personality's ____________________ attitude made it difficult for the station manager to find advertisers.

4. despot (des′ pət)

(*n.*) a ruler who oppresses his or her subjects, a tyrant

That film director is known for acting like a ____________________ on the movie set.

5. haggle (hag′ əl)

(*v.*) to argue in a petty way, especially about a price

Let's not ____________________ over the price of admission until we finish writing the play!

6. harmonious (här mō′ nē əs)

(*adj.*) able to get along together well; combining different elements that blend pleasingly; melodious

The two companies' negotiations were ____________________ and resulted in a merger.

7. legacy (leg′ ə sē)

(*n.*) an inheritance; something handed down from an ancestor or from the past

The ____________________ from her grandmother made her a wealthy woman.

8. partial (pär′ shəl)

(*adj.*) not complete; favoring one side over another; showing a strong liking for someone or something

To say that she is ____________________ to sweets would be an understatement.

9. patronize (pa′ trə nīz)

(*v.*) to give one's business to regularly as a customer; to support, provide financial help; to treat someone as an inferior while making a show of being kind or gracious

We like to ____________________ the family-owned stores in the neighborhood.

10. rite (rīt)

(*n.*) a ceremony; the customary form of a ceremony; any formal custom or practice

A minister will perform the marriage ____________________.

Using Context

*For each item, determine whether the **boldface** word from pages 218–219 makes sense in the context of the sentence. Circle the item numbers next to the six sentences in which the words are used correctly.*

1. The mayor of the city declared that the local hero's birthday would be a holiday on which the community would celebrate his **legacy** of bravery.

2. The principal is thought of as a **despot** in our school, as he is able to act as a mentor and a friend when it is appropriate.

3. I **haggled** with my sister until she caved and told me all about plans for the surprise party.

4. I'm quite surprised at how successful my business has been, as when I started it I feared I would be **bankrupt** within a year.

5. On the last day of school, the teacher was touched to read all of the thank-you notes from students who claimed to **patronize** her and said that they would miss her class.

6. Even though the two companies are competitors, they were able to work in a **harmonious** way to raise money for an important cause.

7. Their stories **coincide** so perfectly that I wonder if they planned out what to say together beforehand.

8. The **rite** before the musical usually gives a preview of all the songs you will hear in the show.

9. While I know we would have fun at either the beach or the amusement park, I am **partial** to swimming in the ocean.

10. It's truly amazing that in spite of the hard times she has endured, she shows no proof of being at all **cynical**.

Choosing the Right Word

*Select the **boldface** word that better completes each sentence. You might refer to the passage on pages 212–213 to see how most of these words are used in context. Note that the choices might be related forms of the Unit words.*

1. The city is hosting a conference to celebrate Mark Twain's (**legacy, rite**) and discuss his landmark novels and witty essays.

2. A party that cannot offer new ideas to deal with the pressing problems of the day must be considered politically (**partial, bankrupt**).

3. No matter how efficient the new chairperson may be, the meeting will not proceed (**cynically, harmoniously**) unless the members cooperate.

4. Each answer will be considered either right or wrong; no (**bankrupt, partial**) credit will be given.

5. Isn't it (**cynical, harmonious**) of you to ask other people to support a candidate in whom you yourself have no confidence?

6. Why (**haggle, coincide**) over minor details when we are in agreement overall?

7. Although Aunt Helen serves delicious pumpkin pie on Thanksgiving, I must say that I am (**partial, harmonious**) to apple pie.

8. I am annoyed by the (**haggling, patronizing**) way in which they keep reminding me "how a well-bred person behaves."

9. Your healthy body is a (**legacy, rite**) you have received from your parents, and you should strive to protect it from harmful influences.

10. One reason the coach is so popular is that he is firm and even tough with his players but never acts like a (**bankrupt, despot**).

11. Learning to drive, graduating from high school, and entering college or the job market are all part of a teenager's (**rites, despots**) of passage.

12. The jury was impressed by the fact that the testimony of two witnesses who were complete strangers (**coincided, patronized**) in every detail.

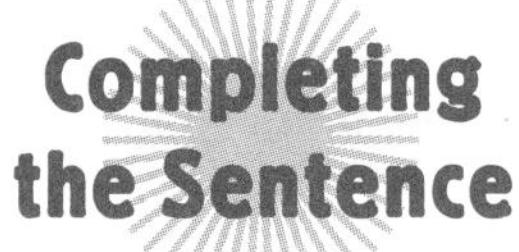

Choose the word from the word bank that best completes each of the following sentences. Write the correct word or form of the word in the space provided.

bankrupt	cynical	haggle	legacy	patronize
coincide	despot	harmonious	partial	rite

1. I think your price for the tennis racket is too high, but as I'm in no mood to ____________ with you, I'll take it.

2. Our supervisor became extremely unpopular with us because he acted like a(n) ____________ toward everyone in the department.

3. The students were urged to ____________ the local merchants who advertised in the school paper.

4. Your program for cleaning up the neighborhood ____________ with ours, so why don't we work together?

5. The pagan religions of ancient times revolved around the performance of various ____________ designed to ensure the fertility of the land.

6. Nothing will be accomplished unless the members of the committee work together in a(n) ____________ fashion.

7. I am making only a(n) ____________ payment at the present time and will pay off the balance in installments.

8. True, business has been poor, but we are covering our expenses and can assure you that there's no danger of our going ____________.

9. When you say that "everyone is out to take advantage of everyone else," I think you're being much too ____________.

10. We must be prepared to defend the ____________ of freedom that we have inherited from earlier generations of Americans.

End Set B

Synonyms

*Choose the word or form of the word from this Unit that is the same or most nearly the same in meaning as the **boldface** word or expression in the phrase. Write that word on the line. Use a dictionary if necessary.*

1. was **ailing** with a headache ____________
2. paid the debt of the **insolvent** company ____________
3. will **conduct** the religious services ____________
4. would **quibble** over a penny ____________
5. passed on his **birthright** to his children ____________
6. **amassed** huge amounts of arsenal ____________
7. did not **concur** with the proposal ____________
8. find a **compatible** mate ____________
9. acted like a **dictator** on the project ____________
10. ignored the **uproar** of the crowd ____________
11. **rugged** soldiers who survived the harsh winters ____________
12. has become **skeptical** of politics ____________
13. was behaving in a **bossy** manner ____________
14. had taken sides in the bitter **dispute** ____________
15. will undergo a **ceremony** of initiation ____________

Antonyms

*Choose the word or form of the word from this Unit that is most nearly opposite in meaning to the **boldface** word or expression in the phrase. Write that word on the line. Use a dictionary if necessary.*

1. made **unjustifiable** accusations ____________
2. submitted the **entire** report ____________
3. a situation that is one of **sadness** ____________
4. met someone who is **respectful** ____________
5. was **foolish** in the choices she made ____________

Writing: Words in Action

Suppose that people used gold as currency today. People's wealth would actually be measured by their "weight in gold." Do you think people would be more conscientious about spending and saving? Write an essay to support your opinion, using details from the reading (pages 212–213) and three or more words from this Unit.

Vocabulary in Context

*Some of the words you have studied in this Unit appear in **boldface** type. Read the passage below, and then circle the letter of the correct answer for each word as it is used in context.*

In 2009 an amateur treasure hunter stumbled upon a startling find in farmland in central England. At the spot where his metal detector buzzed, he dug deep to pull up objects caked in mud. A local historian examining the bounty could not believe his eyes: There were beautiful, ornately engraved gold and silver pieces dating back to Britain's Dark Ages more than a thousand years ago. To say this collection, named the Staffordshire, or Anglo-Saxon, Hoard, was greeted with excitement and **mirth** is an understatement!

But the first find was just the tip of the iceberg. The metal detector had located a **partial** chunk of what archaeologists uncovered next. To date, nearly 4000 fragments and objects have been unearthed, making it the largest hoard of Anglo-Saxon gold ever found. There were bracelets, arm rings, and ornaments for helmets and swords, some embedded with semi-precious stones or delicate lace patterns.

Britain's Anglo-Saxon period lasted about 600 years, from approximately 450 to 1066 CE. While much is known about the time, much still remains a mystery. More than one ruler was a **despot**; others were kinder. Historians believe the treasure trove may reveal more information about the era.

It was the job of a **sagacious** government representative to **officiate** at a hearing to determine who had a claim on the hoard's monetary value. A decision was made that both the treasure hunter and the farmer who owned the field had a legitimate claim, and both men became rich as a result. Meanwhile, the Staffordshire Hoard is on permanent display at several area museums, where many people eagerly **patronize** the exhibits.

---

1. What is the meaning of **mirth** as it is used in paragraph 1?

a. doubt
b. glumness
c. glee
d. suspicion

2. Which word means the same as **partial** as it is used in paragraph 2?

a. not visible
b. not complete
c. not fair
d. not obvious

3. **Despot** comes from the Latin word **despotes**. **Despotes** most likely means

a. master
b. designer
c. expert
d. apprentice

4. The word **sagacious** means about the same as

a. shrewd
b. mature
c. outlawed
d. reliable

5. What is the meaning of **officiate** as it is used in paragraph 4?

a. observe
b. chair
c. approve
d. support

6. What does **patronize** most likely mean as it is used in paragraph 4?

a. view
b. compensate
c. support
d. explore

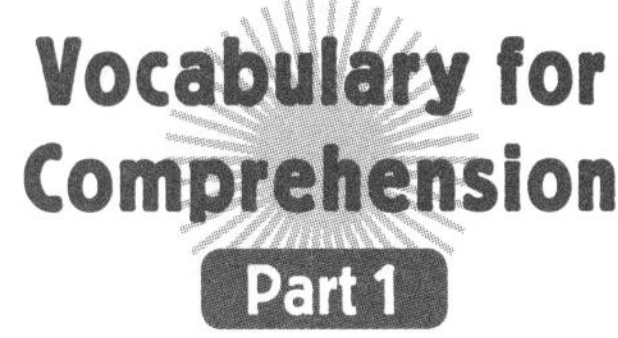

*Read "The Athletic Career of Jim Thorpe," which contains words in **boldface** that appear in Units 13–15. Then answer the questions.*

The Athletic Career of Jim Thorpe

Voted the greatest male athlete of the first half of the twentieth century by the Associated Press in 1950, Jim Thorpe received **massive** praise and criticism in his lifetime.

Thorpe was born in Indian Territory (now Oklahoma) in 1888. His father was a farmer. His mother was rumored to be a descendant of Black Hawk, a famous tribal chief, warrior, and athlete.

In 1904, Thorpe was sent to the Carlisle Indian School in Pennsylvania, where his astounding athletic ability was first discovered by Glenn S. "Pop" Warner, the legendary coach of the school. When the coach spotted Thorpe high-jumping six feet, he offered him a place on the track team. Thorpe instantly became a star. He also became a football hero. In fact, in one of his best games, he helped the Carlisle football team **vanquish** its rival Harvard by booting four field goals. For his efforts on the football field, he was named to the All-American team.

Jim Thorpe left Carlisle in 1909 to play baseball for two seasons in the East Carolina minor league, a decision that would affect his whole life. However, his greatest achievement would come in the 1912 Olympic Games in Stockholm, Sweden. There, he would win two gold medals—in the pentathlon and the decathlon. The pentathlon involved five events: a long jump, a javelin throw, a 200-meter dash, a discus throw, and a 1,500-meter dash. The decathlon had ten events: a 100-meter dash, a long jump, a shot put throw, a high jump, a 400-meter dash, 110-meter hurdles, a discus throw, a pole vault, a javelin throw, and a 1,500-meter run! The **magnitude** of winning both the pentathlon and the decathlon was undeniable.

"Sir, you are the greatest athlete in the world," said King Gustav V of Sweden, who was **officiating** at the games. Yet as events would show, Thorpe's triumph would be only a **partial** victory.

Shortly after the Olympic games were held, a sportswriter who had seen Thorpe play baseball in the minor leagues exposed him as a professional athlete, making him ineligible for Olympic competition. The Amateur Athletic Union stripped Thorpe of his Olympic records and medals in 1913, casting a **pall** over his achievements.

Thorpe joined the baseball team the New York Giants in that same year. The versatile Thorpe played professionally in both baseball and football. He was named the first commissioner of the new National Football League in 1920.

For his achievements in football, he was inducted into the College and Pro Football Halls of Fame. In 1982, almost 30 years after his death in 1953, the International Olympic Committee restored Thorpe's medals, thereby preserving his status as one of the world's greatest athletes.

1. What does the word **massive** most likely mean as it is used in line 4?
   A) reliable
   B) enthusiastic
   C) great
   D) widespread

2. Based on the passage, when was Jim Thorpe's athletic ability first recognized?
   A) when he was a pro football player
   B) when he was at the Carlisle Indian School
   C) when he played for the New York Giants
   D) when he was a gold medal winner

3. Which word means the opposite of **vanquish** in line 21?
   A) challenge
   B) surrender
   C) conquer
   D) throw

4. Which phrase is closest in meaning to the word **magnitude** as it is used in line 41?
   A) minor significance
   B) exceptional talent
   C) extreme generosity
   D) great importance

5. What is the meaning of **officiating** as used in line 46?
   A) competing
   B) announcing
   C) presiding
   D) voting

6. What does the phrase **partial** victory in line 48 most likely suggest?
   A) It was an instant win.
   B) It was an elusive victory.
   C) It was a cherished achievement.
   D) It was an incomplete victory.

7. How did Thorpe's decision to play pro baseball "affect his whole life" (line 28)?
   A) It interfered with his personal life.
   B) It deprived him of his Olympic medals.
   C) It cost him a job as football commissioner.
   D) It led to him winning two gold medals.

8. Which sentence from the passage **best** supports the conclusion that Olympic competitors had to be amateur athletes?
   A) "greatest achievement would come in the 1912 Olympic Games" (lines 29–30)
   B) "a sportswriter who had seen Thorpe play baseball in the minor leagues exposed him" (lines 50–52)
   C) "Thorpe joined the baseball team the New York Giants" (lines 58–59)
   D) "the International Olympic Committee restored Thorpe's medals (lines 67–69)

9. **Part A**
   Which word is closest in meaning to the word **pall** as it is used in line 56?
   A) bore
   B) shadow
   C) scandal
   D) fascination

   Part B
   Which sentence from "The Athletic Career of Jim Thorpe" provides the **best** clue to the meaning of the word **pall**?
   A) "his greatest achievement would come in the 1912 Olympic Games" (lines 28–30)
   B) "'you are the greatest athlete in the world (lines 44–45)
   C) "Thorpe's triumph would be only a partial victory" (lines 47–48)
   D) "Thorpe joined the baseball team" (line 58)

10. How does the author primarily structure "The Athletic Career of Jim Thorpe"?
   A) using cause-effect
   B) in chronological order
   C) in order of importance
   D) using comparison-contrast

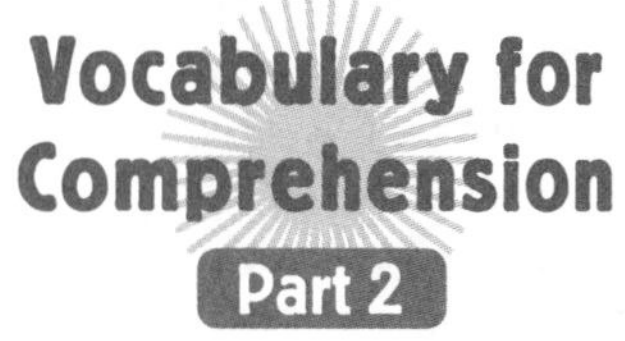

*Read this passage, which contains words in **boldface** that appear in Units 13–15. Then choose the best answer to each question based on what is stated or implied in the passage. You may refer to the passage as often as necessary.*

Questions 1–10 are based on the following passage.

It is said that you will never get two people in Buenos Aires to agree on how tango began. The emotional and intensely dramatic dance and its music have generated a **hoard** of myths, legends, and tall stories as rich and **enchanting** as the city where it was born.

There is no disputing the history that surrounds the origins of tango. When Argentina achieved unification and peace in 1861, most of the country was virtually unpopulated. Large areas of Argentina were made up of vast, open prairies, known as the *pampas*. **Hardy** Argentine cowboys, known as *gauchos*, followed enormous herds of cattle as they roamed these rich grasslands. In its first year, the new government was **sagacious** in employing engineers to create a railroad system that covered the whole country. The Argentine state took possession of the *pampas*, and sold the land to farmers, who bred the cattle for beef. Cattle were brought into Buenos Aires on railroad cars, and they left the city in container ships as refrigerated beef. In less than forty years, beef exports turned Argentina into the seventh most prosperous nation in the world.

In 1880, Buenos Aires was a town with 210,000 inhabitants. By 1910 it was a **cosmopolitan** city with a population of 1.2 million. European workers—mainly Spaniards, Italians, French, and Germans—came to work in British-built meat-packing plants. *Gauchos* who had lost their way of life on the *pampas* joined them. The immigrants worked hard, blended **harmoniously**, and settled in *barrios*—neighborhoods on the edges of the city. Argentina's great writer Jorge Luis Borges (1899–1986) wrote that the real story of Buenos Aires is told in the development of its *barrios*. The music that the new citizens made together was about love and loss, nostalgia and passion. They created their song lyrics out of *lunfardo*, the tough street-slang of the port city. The guitars, fiddles and drums of their native cultures blended into something new. It was, however, a small German concertina called a *bandoneón* that gave the tango its characteristic sound. The *bandoneón* is both assertive and melancholy. Its staccato rhythms dissolve naturally into showers of notes in a way that make it a perfect accompaniment to the quick walking steps, abrupt stops, and graceful slides of the dance.

Tango has never been quite **reputable**, but it is universally **revered**. In 2009 its unique **legacy** of music and dance to the world was recognized by UNESCO as part of the Cultural Heritage of Humanity. As Borges said, the people of Buenos Aires recognize themselves in tango completely, and people all over the world recognize Buenos Aires in it—whether they have been there or not. The composer and bandleader Astor Piazzolla (1921–1992) once said, "Whether you are in Paris, London, or Rome, as long as the music lasts, you are in Buenos Aires." Borges put it like this: "Without the streets or dusks of Buenos Aires, a tango cannot be written."

1. As it is used in line 18, "sagacious" most nearly means
   A) optimistic.
   B) thrifty.
   C) tolerant.
   D) smart.

2. As it is used in line 32, "cosmopolitan" most nearly means
   A) showing Italian influence.
   B) created artificially.
   C) international in character.
   D) well-traveled.

3. The author quotes Jorge Luis Borges in order to
   A) show how the tango is admired by writers and artists.
   B) make the tango seem more reputable.
   C) explain the relationship between tango and Buenos Aires.
   D) reveal the personal tastes of Argentina's greatest writer.

4. According to Borges, the history of Buenos Aires is found in the
   A) unification of Argentina.
   B) development of the railways.
   C) export of refrigerated beef.
   D) people who live in the city.

5. Which choice provides the best evidence for the answer to the previous question?
   A) Lines 9–12 ("When... unpopulated")
   B) Lines 17–20 ("In its... whole country")
   C) Lines 26–29 ("In less...in the world")
   D) Lines 37–40 ("The immigrants...*barrios*")

6. Paragraph 3 (lines 30–59) suggests that by 1910 the population of Buenos Aires was
   A) largely composed of immigrants from Europe and the *pampas.*
   B) employed in the meat-packing industry.
   C) mostly employed on the railroads.
   D) preoccupied with the creation of tango.

7. As it is used in line 60, "reputable" most nearly means
   A) prosperous.
   B) international.
   C) respectable.
   D) easy.

8. As it is used in line 62, "legacy" most nearly means
   A) advancement.
   B) gift.
   C) combination.
   D) inheritance.

9. The last paragraph claims that tango
   A) can only be fully understood by the people of Buenos Aires.
   B) now belongs to the whole world, and not just Argentina.
   C) evokes the spirit of Buenos Aires, wherever it is heard.
   D) has turned the entire world into Buenos Aires.

10. The main purpose of the passage is to
    A) celebrate the spirit of the city of Buenos Aires.
    B) give the historical circumstances of tango's origins.
    C) show how the music of the *barrios* became world famous.
    D) explain the birth of tango in Buenos Aires.

From the word bank below, choose the word that has the same or nearly the same meaning as the ***boldface*** *word in each sentence and write it on the line. You will not use all of the words.*

akin	**elongate**	**harmonious**	**magnitude**
blurt	**fluctuate**	**hoax**	**maternal**
chronological	**gala**	**ignite**	**oppress**
coincide	**gratitude**	**impostor**	**vanquish**

1. My mother warned me not to **blab** anything about my father's surprise birthday party. ________________

2. Although the two people have such different personalities, they're still able to work together in an **agreeable** fashion. ________________

3. As I went to write notes to the people who had donated to my cause, I found I couldn't find the words to properly express my **thanks**. ________________

4. I was determined to **conquer** my fear of heights so that I could go on a helicopter ride with my family. ________________

5. The literature teacher often relates current events to the stories her students are reading to **kindle** their interest in classic novels. ________________

6. My feelings on the subject continue to **waver** with every new piece of information that comes out. ________________

7. I wondered whether I should structure my essay by discussing the events in **consecutive** order or by breaking them up by theme. ________________

8. The **immensity** of the project required almost all of my time, and I feared that I would fall behind in my other classes. ________________

9. The guidance counselor's **protective** aura made her students trust her and turn to her for comfort. ________________

10. When I entered the room and saw the impressive décor, I once again couldn't believe I had been invited to this **spectacular** awards ceremony. ________________

11. The detective warned that he would find a way to prove the true identity of the **trickster**. ________________

12. Since our preferences in novels always seem to **match**, why don't we start a book club? ________________

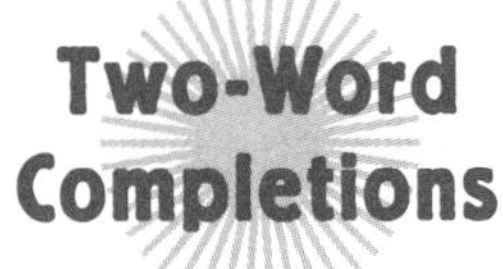

Select the pair of words that best completes the meaning of each of the following sentences.

1. Betty's grandfather was a __________ young man who traveled alone on a ship from Ireland to the United States. Although he worked years for __________ wages, he eventually saved up enough money to buy a farm and start a family.

a. hilarious ... bankrupt
b. cynical ... stodgy
c. wan ... inflated
d. hardy ... meager

2. "I hate to __________ over minor details," the fussy little prince remarked to the court magician. "But I'm hungry, and bouquets of fake flowers aren't particularly __________. Do you have any carrot sticks?"

a. grovel ... pedestrian
b. clamor ... gaudy
c. haggle ... nutritious
d. meditate ... massive

3. The referees who __________ at hockey games are like judges presiding over trials. For that reason, they and their assistants must be as __________ as possible. If they show any favoritism in their calls, they'll hear about it from the fans.

a. agitate ... authoritative
b. officiate ... impartial
c. haggle ... partial
d. clamor ... cosmopolitan

4. "I'm happy to shop at an establishment that is owned by a __________ professional," Mom declared. "But I absolutely refuse to __________ a store that is run by people who are out to cheat me."

a. reputable ... patronize
b. despotic ... bankrupt
c. legitimate ... transmit
d. cosmopolitan ... foster

5. "If we are to win this important election," the senator said, "we must put aside our private __________ and present a united front. Those who __________ this advice will be helping our cause."

a. legacies ... revere
b. handicrafts ... countenance
c. feuds ... heed
d. afflictions ... diminish

6. "You certainly don't have to __________ your money the way a miser would," I observed, "but if you continue to throw it around quite so freely, you'll soon be __________."

a. revere ... pedestrian
b. foster ... indisposed
c. transmit ... stodgy
d. hoard ... bankrupt

7. The tragic news of our friend's death in an automobile accident cast a(n) __________ of gloom over our little gathering that evening and turned our __________ to tears.

a. pall ... mirth
b. saga ... countenance
c. clamor ... agitation
d. affliction ... rite

Idioms

In the passage "Celebrating the Death of a Killer" (see pages 200–201), the writer states that the World Health Organization's goal to eradicate smallpox was considered by many to be "beyond the pale."

"Beyond the pale" is an idiom that means the idea was so extreme, it was unacceptable to many people. An **idiom** is an expression that does not make sense if you define it literally. Idioms work their way into our daily language. The best way to learn idioms is to understand the context in which they are used.

Choosing the Right Idiom

Read each sentence. Use context clues to figure out the meaning of each idiom in ***boldface*** *print. Then write the letter of the definition for the idiom in the sentence.*

1. With the flu going around, students at our school are **dropping like flies**. _______
2. Your stationary bike is a **white elephant** that sits in the garage collecting dust. _______
3. With increased gas and food prices, we must **tighten our belts** around here. _______
4. I'm not sure why Steve called this meeting, but I think he has **something up his sleeve**. _______
5. John will do anything for Brenda **at the drop of a hat**. _______
6. Did you hear that Jack **threw his hat into the ring** and decided to run for class president? _______
7. "Quit **horsing around** before you knock over the display!" Maya said. _______
8. Whenever Carlos is out of town, Sheila acts as if she is **top dog**. _______
9. If Mark thinks I will lend him money, he's **barking up the wrong tree**. _______
10. When Dana takes over Jessica's job, she will have some pretty **big shoes to fill**. _______

a. announced a run for office

b. a secret plan or scheme

c. looking for something in the wrong place

d. becoming ill or dying in large numbers

e. possession that cost too much but has little value

f. playing rowdily or acting silly

g. the person who is in charge

h. promptly or immediately

i. huge expectations in taking the place of another

j. spend less money than usual.

Classical Roots

rupt—to break

This Latin root appears in **bankrupt** (page 218). Literally, the word means "bank broken"—that is, "unable to pay one's debts." It also means "one who is unable to pay his or her debts" or "to ruin financially and thus make unable to pay debts." Some other words based on the same root are listed below.

abrupt	**disruptive**	**incorruptible**	**irruption**
corrupt	**erupt**	**interrupt**	**rupture**

From the list of words above, choose the one that corresponds to each of the brief definitions below. Write the word in the blank space in the illustrative sentence below the definition. Use a dictionary if necessary.

1. sudden, short, blunt; very steep
The car made a(n) ____________________ stop at the crosswalk to avoid hitting the pedestrian.

2. rotten, wicked, dishonest; to make evil; to bribe
The ____________________ dictatorship was replaced by a democratic republic.

3. to break in upon; to stop, halt
All day long she has to ____________________ her work in order to answer telephone calls from clients.

4. to burst forth (*"to break out"*)
Boiling streams of lava ____________________ from the exploding volcano, causing the population to flee.

5. not open to immoral behavior, honest; unbribable
He remained a(n) ____________________ public official despite the many attempts of the crime boss to bribe him.

6. a breaking; to break
The engineers worked frantically to repair the ____________________ in the wall of the dam.

7. causing disorder or turmoil (*"to break apart"*)
His late arrival had a(n) ____________________ influence on the meeting.

8. a breaking or bursting in; a violent invasion
The ____________________ of the Goths into Roman territory led to the collapse of the Roman Empire.

FINAL MASTERY TEST

Synonyms

Select the two words or expressions that are most nearly the same in meaning.

1. a. fickle **b.** vital **c.** indispensable **d.** docile

2. a. quench **b.** seethe **c.** stifle **d.** bewilder

3. a. reputable **b.** animated **c.** available **d.** spirited

4. a. foretaste **b.** magnitude **c.** overture **d.** preview

5. a. lubricate **b.** decrease **c.** diminish **d.** capsize

6. a. disrupt **b.** foster **c.** haggle **d.** nurture

7. a. hinder **b.** mortify **c.** brood **d.** meditate

8. a. inimitable **b.** unique **c.** ultimate **d.** cynical

9. a. despot **b.** turmoil **c.** dynasty **d.** regime

10. a. renovate **b.** indulge **c.** pamper **d.** erode

11. a. customary **b.** notorious **c.** orthodox **d.** quaint

12. a. harmonious **b.** mellow **c.** futile **d.** fruitless

13. a. hoard **b.** remnant **c.** cache **d.** void

14. a. alliance **b.** pact **c.** potential **d.** wrath

15. a. implore **b.** verify **c.** goad **d.** entreat

Antonyms

Select the two words or expressions that are most nearly opposite in meaning.

16. a. lavish **b.** inflammable **c.** meager **d.** nutritious

17. a. random **b.** chronological **c.** pending **d.** graphic

18. a. hilarious **b.** hostile **c.** heartrending **d.** hardy

19. a. insinuate **b.** dissuade **c.** accelerate **d.** entice

20. a. presume **b.** enchant **c.** pall **d.** trickle

21. a. gigantic **b.** peevish **c.** puny **d.** disputatious

22. a. flounder **b.** singe **c.** wilt **d.** flourish

23. a. grovel **b.** hanker **c.** patronize **d.** hurtle

24. a. veto **b.** maul **c.** ratify **d.** swerve

25. a. leisurely **b.** miscellaneous **c.** humdrum **d.** grueling

Select the pair of words that best completes the meaning of each of the following sentences.

26. Although the experienced ____________ had a highly marketable idea, he ____________ in the recession.

a. fugitive ... was vigilant
b. beneficiary ... was controversial
c. entrepreneur ... went bankrupt
d. bystander ... was sullen

27. With her ____________ complexion and ____________ dress, the actress resembled the ghost of a vaudevillian entertainer.

a. dynamic ... maternal
b. wayward ... trivial
c. wan ... gaudy
d. lethargic ... grimy

28. The man was sure the watch was a valuable collectible and was shocked to find out that he had been ____________ as it was nothing but a ____________.

a. duped ... counterfeit
b. flustered ... farce
c. heeded ... drone
d. evicted ... firebrand

29. The editor's comment about the novel's "____________" narrative ____________ the writer.

a. unscathed ... inflated
b. stodgy ... disheartened
c. gruesome ... marred
d. notable ... frustrated

30. Although the famous ballplayer's signature on the ball brought up for appraisal was barely ____________ an expert was able to confirm that it was ____________.

a. legible ... legitimate
b. amiss ... clarification
c. literate ... makeshift
d. substantial ... tactful

31. Even when the outlook was ____________ the experienced captain never showed any sign of ____________ as he commanded his crew.

a. homicide ... melancholy
b. grim ... agitation
c. literate ... makeshift
d. fallible ... indifference

32. Although Emma's performance on the pianoforte was ____________ she could not hope to be considered truly ____________.

a. regal ... reluctant
b. hospitable ... gigantic
c. adequate ... proficient
d. gala ... infamous

Supplying Words in Context

To complete each sentence, select the best word from among the choices given. Not all words in the word bank will be used. You may modify the word form as necessary.

adjacent	**flagrant**	**inflict**	**nomadic**
blurt	**fledgling**	**interrogate**	**nub**
botch	**impostor**	**malignant**	**pervade**
dominate	**indignant**	**mull**	**uncertainty**

33. Although I realize you have many interesting stories to tell, I do wish you wouldn't always ____________________ the conversation.

34. Inexperienced as we were, we knew we would ____________________ the preparation of the meal, so we decided to go out to eat.

35. I have to ____________________ over today's events to determine if I had acted inappropriately.

36. Instead of giving me unimportant details, let's get to the ____________________ of the matter.

37. When I was a(n) ____________________ in my first pro season, a veteran player mentored me.

38. Although his house is ____________________ to the school, he is often late for his first class.

affliction	**downright**	**interminable**	**recompense**
alight	**elongate**	**iota**	**snare**
casual	**incentive**	**malady**	**transmit**
dilapidated	**insubordinate**	**morbid**	**utmost**

39. The trick was to ____________________ him in his own web of lies and deceit.

40. It was ____________________ rude of her to ignore my kind offer of help.

41. Luckily, the communications officer was able to ____________________ an SOS signal.

42. The old cabin was ____________________ and looked as if it might blow over in a strong wind.

43. Her grateful smile was ample ____________________ for the time I had spent in helping her.

44. If you had a(n) ____________________ of consideration, you would turn down the volume on the TV.

*Select the word or expression that best completes the meaning of the sentence or answers the question, with particular reference to the meaning of the word in **boldface** type.*

45. A person who receives a **legacy** has gained something as a result of
a. dishonesty
b. gambling
c. inheriting it
d. working for it

46. Which of the following would *not* be found in **rural** areas?
a. water
b. skyscrapers
c. people
d. cows

47. Which of the following is likely to be **sodden**?
a. a rain-soaked field
b. a driver's test
c. a desert
d. a school musical

48. An example of a **grim** event is a
a. holiday
b. family reunion
c. fatal accident
d. graduation

49. You would be most likely to **browse**
a. when you are asleep
b. during a test
c. on the tennis court
d. in a library

50. A **stalemate** lacks
a. a sense of humor
b. a solution
c. opponents
d. freshness

51. If there is **mutual** admiration between two people,
a. the admiration is one-sided
b. the admiration will not last
c. the admiration is not genuine
d. they admire each other

52. A person facing the **hazards** of life is
a. tackling perils
b. making money
c. playing golf
d. winning victories

53. A **braggart** would be most likely to
a. toot his or her own horn
b. fly off the handle
c. grin and bear it
d. stick to his or her guns

54. Which of the following is *not* **transparent**?
a. air
b. a wooden door
c. a pane of glass
d. a feeble excuse

55. Which of the following would be most likely to create **havoc**?
a. a game of volleyball
b. a summer breeze
c. a tornado
d. a school assembly

56. Which of the following would *not* be likely to **canvass** an area?
a. a pollster
b. a door-to-door salesperson
c. an interviewer
d. a homebody

Choosing the Right Meaning

Read each sentence carefully. Then select the item that best completes the statement below the sentence.

57. Because both children loved broccoli, their mother did not expect them to **detest** cauliflower.

The word **detest** most nearly means

a. welcome **b.** understand **c.** know **d.** hate

58. The **downtrodden** workers met in the square to talk about the possibility of creating a union.

The word **downtrodden** most nearly means

a. oppressed **b.** well-paid **c.** happy **d.** skillful

59. The dogs pelted out of the house once they saw that the door had been left **ajar**.

The word **ajar** most nearly means

a. untouched **b.** sealed **c.** partly open **d.** alone

60. The longer two people carry on a **feud**, the harder it becomes for them to reconcile.

The word **feud** most nearly means

a. constituent **b.** machine **c.** quarrel **d.** movement

61. As he had been found guilty of **perjury** in the past, his testimony could not be considered reliable, and he was dismissed from the case.

The word **perjury** most nearly means

a. stealing **b.** lying **c.** killing **d.** kidnapping

62. The gift came from an **anonymous** donor, so we could not send out a letter of thanks.

The word **anonymous** most nearly means

a. angry **b.** innocent **c.** eager **d.** unnamed

63. Realizing her brother was the defendant, she knew she would not be able to provide an **impartial** decision, and asked to be removed from the case.

The word **impartial** most nearly means

a. effective **b.** unbiased **c.** incomplete **d.** unhurried

64. She hoped to develop a more **cosmopolitan** point of view by travelling abroad.

The word **cosmopolitan** most nearly means

a. oppressed **b.** mechanical **c.** sophisticated **d.** false

65. The fisherman decided to move to a town by a sea that was rumored to **abound** with fish.

The word **abound** most nearly means

a. be plentiful **b.** be polluted **c.** be reinforced **d.** be domestic

WORD LIST

The following is a list of all the words taught in the Units of this book. The number after each entry indicates the page on which the word is defined.

WORD LIST

INDEX